Design and Make Moving Toys & Models

Adrienne Dawes

INTRODUCTION

Toys and models that move hold a fascination for children of all ages, the fascination lies in the movement of the model and the children's natural curiosity makes them want to investigate how the movement is achieved.

No matter what experiences of cutting, shaping, joining and combining construction materials the pupils have, the challenge of creating a three dimensional model that moves is an exciting and rewarding use of their skills.

Using a variety of construction materials as a means of teaching Design & Technology harnesses enthusiasm and enables work of a high quality to be produced. Opportunities to make models that move occur many times throughout the school year, linked to a variety of topics, and this provides children with a real purpose for their work.

Once the basic skills and techniques have been introduced, then the pupil's own creativity can be left to flourish and the teacher must ensure that:-

• The project / task given to the pupils is demanding enough to allow them to perform at a higher level.

• The task is interesting so that the pupils are encouraged to persist.

• A variety of equipment is available to ensure appropriate choices can be made.

• All equipment and materials are available in the class and they are easily accessible so as to ensure pupils make the correct decisions.

• Sufficient time is allowed to enable thorough experimentation by individuals, that they can practice newly acquired skills, be taught how to correctly use any new pieces of equipment, develop ideas and apply finishing techniques.

• The teacher needs to have the skills and knowledge necessary to intervene when appropriate.

Experimentation and choice on the part of the pupil is very important. This book contains photocopiable resources and teacher / pupil instructions, which will enable you to teach and practice a variety of skills and techniques appropriate to the making of Toys and Models that Move.

The activities are designed to assist adults when introducing new techniques to Key Stage one and Key Stage two pupils and when used by a whole school will ensure progression.

The activities are intended to be used as an introduction and when the pupils have completed these introductory activities they should be provided with a range of materials and equipment to enable them to apply their skills in a Design and Make task and create their own Models that Move.

Copyright © 1997 Adrienne Dawes

Illustrated by Adrienne Dawes and Paul Sealey
Printed in Great Britain for "Topical Resources", Publishers of Educational Materials, P.O. Box 329, Broughton, Preston. PR3 5LT
(Tel/Fax 01772 863158)
by T.Snape & Co, Ltd., Boltons Court, Preston.
Cover Design: Paul Sealey Illustration & Design.

First Published May 1997
ISBN 1 872977 16 2

Teacher Preparation

The techniques needed to create the toys and models that move can be taught to groups or individual pupils depending upon their age and previous experience. You will need to know the children's experience level in the following skills and practice if necessary: Cutting, measuring, joining, combining, disassembling and finishing.

Pupils need to be made aware of the properties of a wide variety of construction materials e.g wood, plastic, card etc. It is important that pupils experiment with materials and equipment before being expected to produce a quality model.

Cutting.

A variety of cutting tools should be introduced to the pupils as and when appropriate for the individuals development and need. Some of these tools need to be used by the pupils under close supervision or their use demonstrated by adults only. This should be decided by individual schools and great care should always be taken when using craft knives and circle cutters as both of these contain sharp blades which will easily cut flesh.

Measuring.

The photocopiable sheets contain pieces that the pupils will use to measure a variety of materials to ensure accurate cutting and shaping. Later when the pupils gain greater confidence and maturity the need for standard measurements will be necessary to complete the more complicated techniques.

Joining.

The pupils should experiment with joining materials in a variety of ways and with a variety of fixings that will allow movement e.g. axle holders made from cable clips or felt pen barrels, hinges made from card and scored corrugated plastic etc. They should test adhesives to discover which works best and which can be used to create permanent or temporary fixings e.g. glue, carpet tape etc.

Combining

Many different materials will be used to create the toys and models that move. Stiff and flexible sheet materials will be combined and pupils need to experiment with all the materials to discover the most suitable for a specific task. A variety of activities can be incorporated into the Design and Make tasks which have direct links to the Science Programmes of Study. These activities should test for example:

- whether or not the materials are waterproof.
- if the chosen materials will float.
- how strong are the chosen materials?
- what load will they hold?
- how can they be strengthened?
- how heavy / light are the materials?

- how will heat or cold effect the working properties of the materials?

There are many tests that should be devised at first by the teacher but later at Key Stage 2 the pupils themselves should create tests for a range of materials in a variety of ways to determine the most suitable for a given task.

Disassembling

An important part of the Design and Technology process is the investigation and disassembling of a variety of objects by the pupils. These tasks should be closely linked to the Design and Make activities in which the pupils will be involved. Manufactured and teacher prepared items should be investigated and disassembled [taken apart] but the items should be realistic in construction and once disassembled should be re - made. A variety of construction kits can be very useful for this activity.

Finishing

Many models can be made to a high quality and then spoilt when decorated because either the wrong paints are used or not enough time is allowed for the pupils to build up the decoration step by step. Ready mix and powder paints are of limited use for decorating reclaimed materials, wood and plastic. The pupils should experiment with a variety of colourings on a variety of materials:

- pva mixed with paint on cardboard boxes
- ink or dyes on wood
- sand mixed with pva and paint to give a textured finish on boxes etc
- sanding yogurt pots prior to painting

A variety of collage materials adding detail to the model should be added to the base coat when sufficient time has been allowed for the paint to dry.

Construction Techniques for Key Stage 1

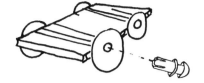

Click Rivets and Corrugated Plastic

Click rivets are made to ensure the free movement of cardboard wheels when used in conjunction with 4mm corrugated plastic. The rivets push into the holes of the corrugated plastic and are very easy to use.

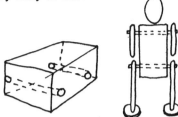

Free Moving Dowel Through a Box

Pupils should be introduced to a bradawl, the correct piece of equipment for making holes in a cardboard box. Once the holes have been made they should be enlarged by using a round file which is pushed in and pulled out until smooth round holes are created through which the 5 mm dowel is pushed and the wheels attached to the ends. This technique can be used to create puppets with moving arms.

New Boxes From Old

Pupils enjoy creating models from junk [reclaimed] materials yet often the finished models are of poor quality as the paint used to decorate them does not cover the writing or decoration on the box. Turning the boxes inside out creates a clean surface which is easily decorated and this is a very useful disassembling task for the pupils.

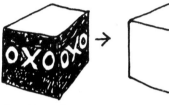

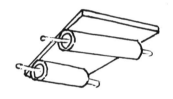

Clip Pegs and Free Moving Dowel

Plastic and wooden clip pegs are cheap to buy and are an effective way of creating holders for free moving dowel. If the holes are too small for the dowel to move freely, then a small piece of felt pen barrel can be placed in the pegs - opening the jaws - and allowing the 5 mm dowel to move freely through the tube.

Felt Pen Barrels and Free Moving Dowel

The barrels from used felt pens are very useful and can be cut using a vice or bench hook and junior hacksaw. They create holders for 5 mm dowel allowing free movement. This technique can be used to create vehicles, windmills, roundabouts and puppets etc.

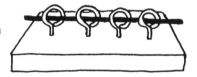

Cotton Reels and Fixed Dowel

The middles of cotton reels can move freely on a fixed piece of dowel to create a variety of moving models. The pupils should drill a 4mm hole in a piece of wood to fix the dowel in place. To create taller models, increase the length of the dowel and glue 2 or more cotton reels on top of each other using a low melt [cool] glue gun.

Screw Eyes and Free Moving Dowel.

Screw eyes create holders for 5 mm dowel allowing free movement. Holes must be made in the wood using a bradawl prior to screwing in the thread to ensure it 'bites' into the wood. A useful technique for holding free moving dowel horizontally and vertically.

Tight Fit Wheels

Most bought wheels are ready drilled with a 4mm hole and this is a tight fit for a 5mm dowel (or even 5.5mm). If a hole is to drilled to create a tight for dowel then use a 4mm drill bit.

Brass Fasteners

Simple brass fasteners can be used to create a joint that allows movement. The pupils should be shown how to create a hole using the pointed end of a pair of scissors (take care!) or pencil point. The brass fastener is pushed through the hole.

Elastic Band Power

Elastic bands are a cheap and efficient way of storing energy to be used for powering toys and models.

Pull-Along Trolley

Technique used:

Click Rivets and 4mm Corrugated Plastic.
(Available from most Educational Technology suppliers.)

Equipment needed:

click rivets 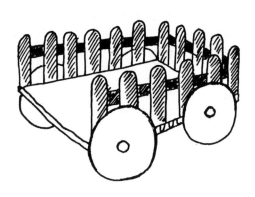   string
4mm corrugated plastic   sticky tape
card wheels
utility snips
     [or craft knife, safety ruler and cutting mat for teacher use only]

How to make the example:

Step 1.   Photocopy the chassis shape opposite and use as a template, one per child.
Step 2.   Draw around the template onto 4mm corrugated plastic or stick the
           template onto the corrugated plastic.
Step 3.   The pupils must be shown how to use the utility snips to cut out the shape of
           the template or the pupils can watch as the teacher cuts out the corrugated
           plastic base using a craft knife, safety ruler and cutting mat.
Step 4.   The teacher should demonstrate to the pupils how the click rivets work.
Step 5.   From a selection of cardboard wheels the pupils should choose four.
Step 6.   The pupils should attach their wheels onto the bases in the position of their
           choice.
Step 7.   Let the pupils test their trolley.
Step 8.   A piece of string should be attached to the front of the trolley with sticky tape.
           The trolley can now be pulled.

How the idea may be developed:
The pupils could be given time to design the shape of their chassis on paper and
provide the teacher with individual patterns from which to cut the bases. Display the
paper patterns with the completed moving base.
Let the pupils test the trolley on slopes, different surfaces and carrying weights etc.
Can the trolley be pushed / pulled to make it move?
Can sides be added to the trolley? How can they be added?
Could the pupils build up boxes on the base to create a vehicle?

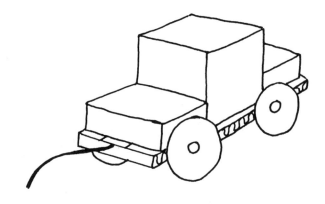

WARNING

Make sure that the lines of the corrugated plastic are lying horizontally along the template, or the click rivets will not be able to be placed in position.

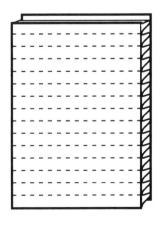

Rotating Legs Figure

Technique used:

Brass fasteners

Equipment needed:

card   brass fasteners
felt pens   scissors

How to make the example:

Step 1.   Photocopy the sheet opposite onto card or paste onto card, one per child.
Step 2.   Decorate the shape and cut it out.
Step 3.   Cut the leg shapes out.
Step 4.   Pierce a hole through the black dots in the centre of the legs and through the black dot marked on the Father Christmas.
Step 5.   Place the legs behind the Father Christmas and line up the holes.
Step 6.   Push a paper fastener through the holes from the front of the figure to the back and open the legs of the fastener to hold the legs in place.
Step 7.   Push the figure and watch the legs move.

How the idea may be developed:

The children can experiment with designing their own figures and different shaped legs.
They could experiment with animals and have two pairs of rotating legs.
Shaped books can be made perhaps during work on transport and these could have rotating wheels attached to the front.

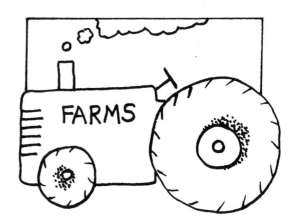

Opening Box

Technique used:

Disassembling - New boxes from old.

Equipment needed:

    variety of cardboard boxes
    glue or masking tape
    scissors

How to make the example:

Step 1.   Let the pupils collect boxes over a period of weeks. Make a display in the classroom. Discuss their size and shape.

Step 2.   The pupils should watch as the teacher disassembles a box by taking it apart at the glued seams.

Step 3.   Discuss with the pupils how a box is created from a flat piece of card.

Step 4.   Let the pupils watch as the teacher remakes the box inside out so that the writing / decoration is on the inside.

Step 5.   Stick the box together along the original seams.

Step 6.   Discuss with the pupils the advantages of this 'new' box. How is it easier to decorate? Why?

Step 7.   The pupils must select a box, disassemble it and make it back up again - inside out.

Step 8.   Photocopy the sheet opposite onto card, one per child.

Step 9.   Carefully cut out the shape along the solid black line.

Step 10. Fold along the dotted lines.

Step 11. The pupils must make up their box by either glueing along the tabs or sticking masking tape along the outside of the seams.

How the idea may be developed:

Make a collection of the 'new' boxes. Display two boxes together which are the same however one should be in its natural state, the othe turned inside out.
The pupils should use these 'new' boxes when making models.
Can the pupils disassemble similar items e.g. envelopes, card folders, pop - up cards?
The pupils could decorate their photocopied net before making up the box.

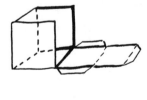

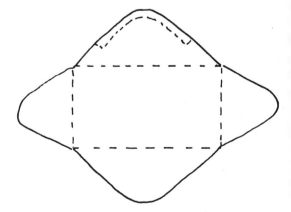

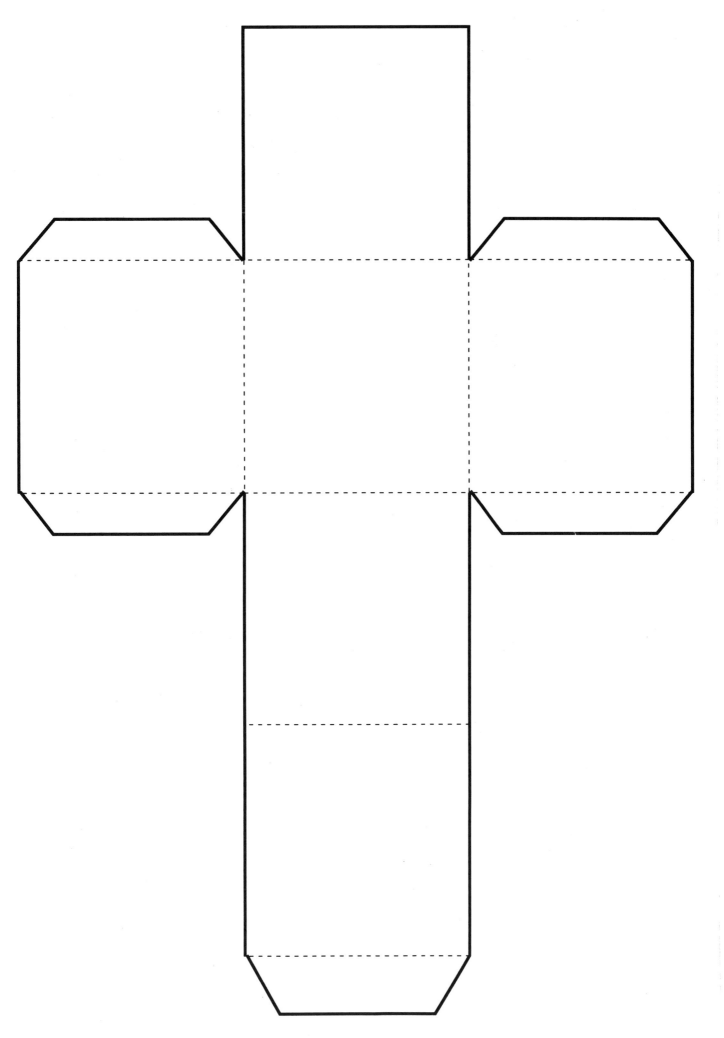

A Thaumatrope

Technique used:

Movement with elastic bands

Equipment needed:

thick card	hole punch
2 elastic bands	felt pens

How to make the example:

Step 1. Photocopy the sheet opposite, one per child.
Step 2. Cut out the first two circles around the thick black lines.
Step 3. Colour in the pictures.
Step 4. Stick the circular pictures onto each side of the thick card and cut the card to the same size.
N.B. Ensure that the black holes on the front are lined up with the black holes on the back of the card circle.
Step 5. Using the hole punch, punch holes through the black dots on the circle.
Step 6. Push one end of an elastic band through the hole forming a loop, and push the other end of the elastic band through the loop.
Step 7. Repeat with the other hole and elastic band.
Step 8. Twist the elastic bands about 20 times, release and look at the pictures.
The lion will appear in the cage.

How the idea may be developed.

Let the pupils experiment with the other pictures and watch the goldfish appear in the bowl and the bird appear in the cage.
Can the pupils draw their own pictures to create a thaumatrope?
A 'wailer' can be made froma thick cardboard circle with holes punched around the edge. The 2 centre holes have a loop of string threaded through them and when twisted and then pulled, the circles will spin creating a wailing sound. Each pull on the string adds force and makes the wailer spin.

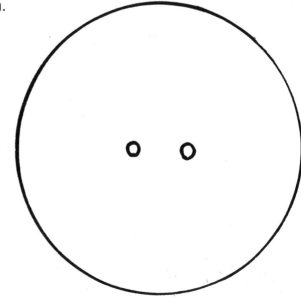

Model Bus

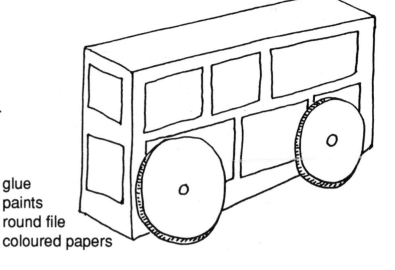

Technique used

Box with holes for free moving dowel.

Equipment needed:

5mm dowel	glue
junior hacksaw	paints
bradawl	round file
vice or bench hook	coloured papers
card	
4mm drilled wooden / plastic / MDF wheels	

How to make the example:

Step 1.   Photocopy the sheet opposite onto card, one per child or stick the photocopy onto card.

Step 2.   Let the pupils decorate their bus.

Step 3.   Show the pupils how to use a bradawl and make 4 holes in the position of the black spots, these will be the axle positions through which the dowel will pass. Let the pupils make the small holes larger with a round file so that the 5mm dowel will be free moving through the body of the bus.

Step 4.   The pupils should make up the net for the body of the bus and glue the seams.

Step 5.   The pupils should measure the dowel for the axles and mark where it is to be cut.

Step 6.   Using either a vice or a bench hook, the pupils should hold the dowel and cut it to the required length using a junior hacksaw.

Step 7.   The cut dowel should then be pushed through the holes and wheels selected by the pupils are then to be placed on the ends of the dowel.

Step 8.   Test the vehicle.

How the idea may be developed:

Boxes could be covered in coloured papers to give the pupils a wider choice and to eliminate the need for painting the bus. Further details could be added by glueing onto the bus e.g windows, headlights etc.
An additional smaller covered box could be glued to the front of the bus to add shape. The pupils could use construction kits to design the bus prior to the making.

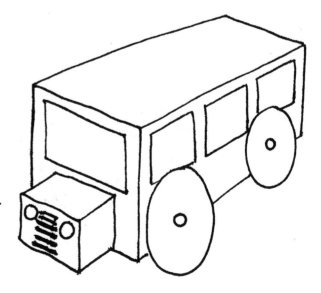

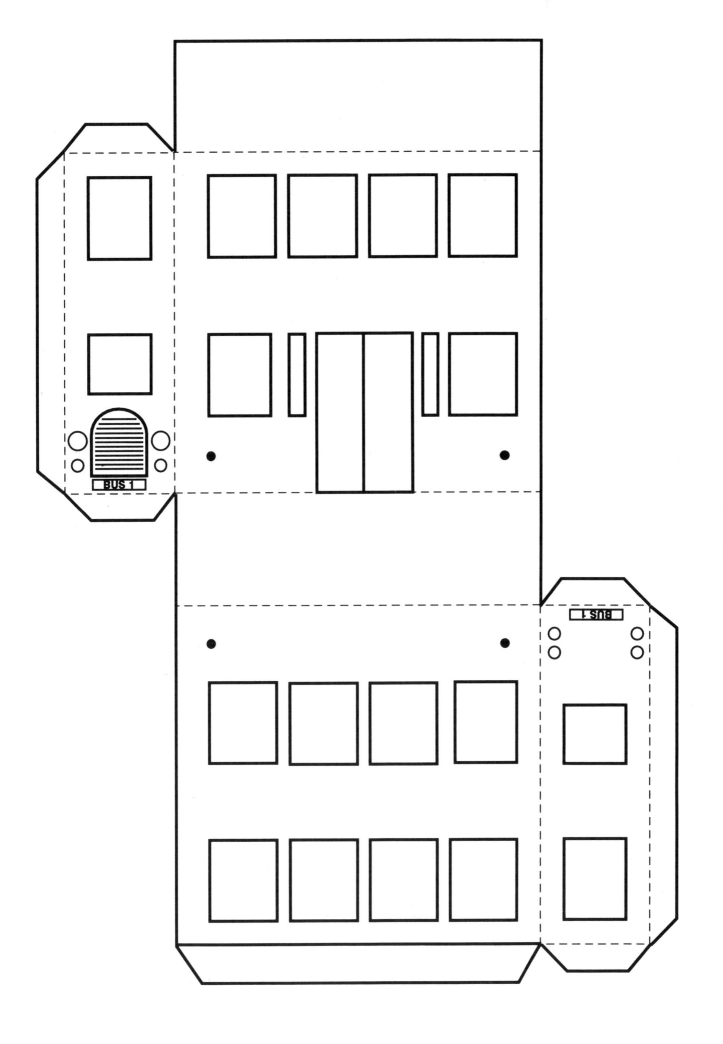

BUS 1

BUS 1

13

Chicken Roundabout

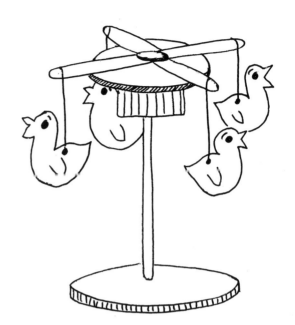

Technique used:

Click Rivets and corrugated plastic

Equipment needed:

4mm corrugated plastic
5mm dowel   card
click rivets   string
junior hacksaw   scissors
vice   lolly sticks
card wheels   felt pens
wooden wheels   sticky tape

How to make the example:

Step 1.   Photocopy the sheet opposite and use the shapes as templates or photocopy the sheet onto card, one per child.

Step 2.   Cut out the shapes along the solid black lines and use template i to cut out a piece of corrugated plastic for the top of the roundabout.

Step 3.   The pupils must be shown how the click rivets work and a card wheel should be attached to one.

Step 4.   Attach the wheel to the corrugated plastic top of the roundabout by pushing the click rivet into one of the channels on the corrugated plastic rectangle Using sticky tape, attach 4 lolly sticks to the card wheel.

Step 5.   Fasten template ii to the dowel and let the pupils cut the dowel to the correct length using a vice and junior hacksaw.

Step 6.   Push the dowel into the bottom edge of the corrugated plastic top.

Step 7.   Push the other end of the dowel into the centre hole of a large wooden wheel, this will form a tight fit and make the base of the roundabout.

Step 8.   Cut the chicken shapes out of card and decorate.

Step 9.   Using sticky tape, fasten string to the four chickens and the chickens to the lolly sticks on the top of the roundabout.

Step 10.   Test the roundabout.

How the idea may be developed:

The pupils could cut a variety of characters from old greetings cards and attach them to the roundabout. The number of lolly sticks extending from the top of the roundabout can be varied and so can the height of the roundabout.

The pupils could create a more stable base by glueing the bottom wheel inside a coffee jar lid or onto a piece of thicker wood.

The string attaching the chickens to the lolly sticks could be tied in place through punched holes.

14

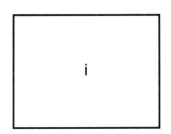

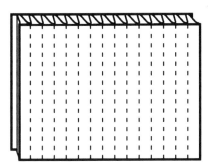

A Model Car

Technique used:

Clip Pegs and Cardboard Base.

Equipment needed:

thick card	clip pegs
5mm dowel	paint
junior hacksaw	glue
utility snips	scissors
used felt pen barrels	vice
low melt [cool] glue gun	
wheels with 4mm drilled holes	

How to make the example:

Step 1.   Photocopy the sheet opposite, one per child.

Step 2.   Paste the shape of the base onto some thick card. Old crisp boxes are very strong and a good source of thick card.

Step 3.   The pupils should select from a variety of boxes which have been turned inside out, to create their cars.(see page 8)

Step 4.   Glue the boxes on to the top side of the base using a paper glue e.g. pva

Step 5.   When dry, the teacher should show the pupils a completed example and using a low melt [cool] glue gun the teacher must glue the clip pegs onto the base of the vehicle in the positions indicated by the dotted lines. (PVA can be used although this takes longer to dry.)

Step 6.   After careful instruction on how to use the equipment, the pupils must estimate the length of the dowel needed to create the axle and this should then be cut using either a vice or a bench hook and a junior hacksaw.

Step 7.   Push the wheels onto the ends of the dowel and place the dowel into the clip pegs. The dowel should be free moving. (Some cheaper pegs may have small holes which do not allow for free moving axles. If this is the case, place the axle through a felt tip pen barrel and clamp the barrel in the pegs. This will allow the axle to be free moving.

Step 8.   The vehicle can now be tested, painted and when dry the finishing touches added e.g. headlights, windows, number plates etc.

How the idea may be developed:

The clip pegs could be glued directly to the base of a box chosen by the pupils. The pupils can draw a pattern for the shape and size of the base of their car onto paper. The teacher can use this to cut out a base from thick cardboard. Spacers made from beads, artstraws, pipe cleaners or tubing can be placed between the wheels and the base of the car to stop the axles sliding around.

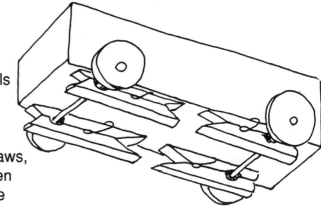

peg

peg

peg

peg

Wind Powered Bat Mobile

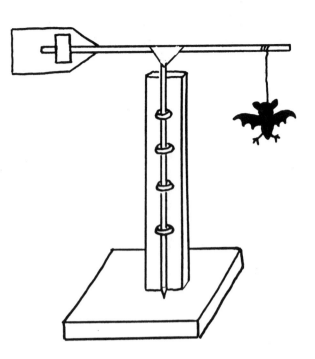

Technique used:

Screw Eyes and free moving dowel.

Equipment needed:

5mm dowel	strip wood
junior hacksaw	thick card
bench hook	bradawl
sticky tape	glue
wool or ribbon	thread
low melt glue gun	utility snips
wooden base approx. 2cm thick	
screw eyes	

How to make the example:

Step 1.   Photocopy the sheet opposite, one per child.

Step 2.   Cut a piece of strip wood of equal length to 'C' on the sheet.

Step 3.   Make 4 equally spaced holes down the length of the strip wood with
          the bradawl and screw the screw eyes into the holes as marked on 'C'.

Step 4.   Glue this centre post onto the base in the space marked 'C'.

Step 5.   Cut 2 pieces of square sectioned wood to the lengths of 'A' and 'B' and
          stick them at either side of the centre post as indicated to give support.

Step 6.   Cut 2 pieces of dowel to the lengths shown on the sheet, the shorter of the
          two is for the centre post, the longer length for the cross section.

Step 7.   Place the shorter length down the centre of the screw eyes and attach the
          middle of the cross section to it using a cool glue gun. Cut two triangle
          shapes from card using the template and glue onto the jointed dowels to
          reinforce the joint.

Step 8.   Cut out the paddle shape and use it as a template to create a card paddle
          which should be attached to one end of the cross section as in the diagram.

Step 9.   Cut out the bat shape and attach thread to the central spot, wrap the other
          end of the thread to the free end of the cross section, securing it firmly.

Step 10. Blow the paddle and watch the bat mobile spin.

How the idea may be developed:

String can be wrapped around the central dowel and when it is pulled quickly it will
make the bat mobile turn.
The bottom tip of the dowel could have a small piece of plastic placed under it to reduce
the friction and therefore make the model go faster.
The pupils can create their own wind powered models using this principal or
anonometers could be created for measuring wind speed during a topic on the Weather.

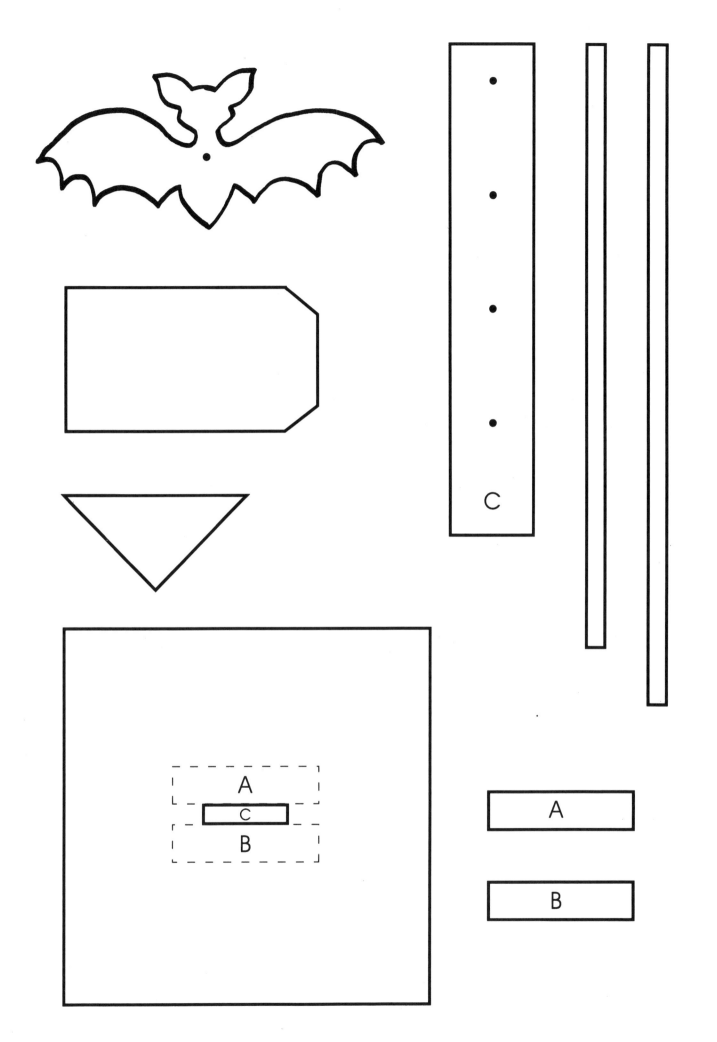

Windmill

Technique used:

Felt Pen Barrels and free moving axles.

Equipment needed:

kitchen roll tube	paints
junior hacksaw	vice
felt pens	bench hook
5mm dowel	pva
low melt [cool] glue gun	4cm diameter wheels

How to make the example:

Step 1. Using a low melt [cool] glue gun, glue a wheel on the top and a wheel on the bottom of a tube from the middle of a kitchen roll.

Step 2. Decorate the tube and top wheel.

Step 3. Using a bench hook and junior hacksaw, the pupils must cut a piece of felt pen barrel 5cm long.

Step 4. Using a low melt [cool] glue gun, the 5cm length of felt pen barrel should be glued across the centre of the top wheel, making sure that 1cm protrudes over the front edge of the tube.

Step 5. Photocopy the sheet opposite, one per child.

Step 6. Decorate the sails for the windmill and cut along the solid black line. Make up the windmill sails as directed on the sheet.

Step 7. Cut a piece of dowel 9cm long.

Step 8. Slide the dowel through the felt pen barrel on the top of the tube and push a wheel onto the front end and a wheel onto the back end of the dowel.

Step 9. Glue the windmill sails to the front wheel.

Step 10. Test the windmill by blowing the sails. Glue the base wheel onto a wooden base to give the windmill more stability.

How the idea may be developed:

The pupils could make smaller / larger sails and test the windmill to see the difference in movement. Could sails be attached to both the front and back wheels?

By allowing the central tower to be free moving on a piece of 3.5mm dowel pushed through the holes in the centre of the top and base wheels, the windmill sails can turn as the windmill rotates. The centre dowel must be pushed into a 3mm drilled hole in the base wood and must be a tight fit to allow no movement.

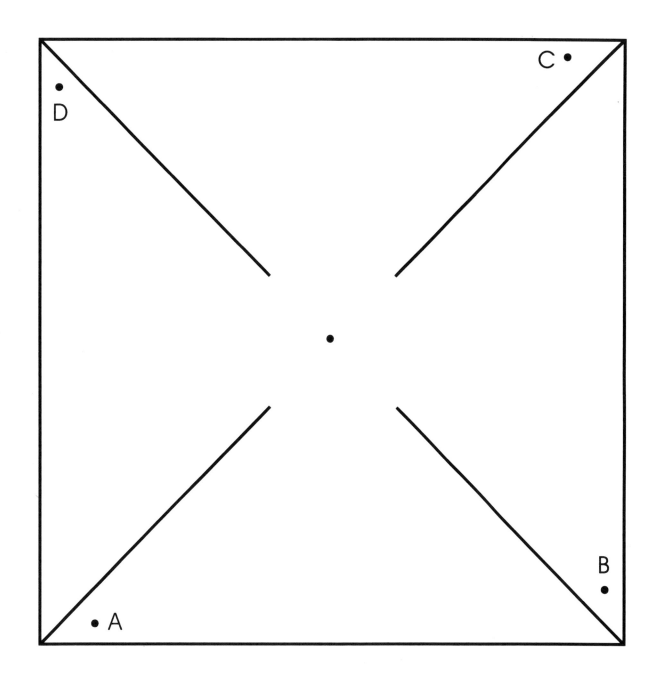

To make the Windmill sails

i   Cut out the square along the solid black lines and decorate front and back.
ii   Cut down the length of the diagonal black lines.
iii   Make holes through the 5 black dots.
iv   Fold A to the centre, line up the holes and glue in place.
v   Fold B to the centre, line up the holes and glue in place.
vi   Fold C to the centre, line up the holes and glue in place.
vii   Fold D to the centre, line up the holes and glue in place.

The sails are now completed and ready to be glued onto the front wheel of the windmill.

Playground See-Saw

Technique used:

Felt Pen Barrels and free moving dowel.

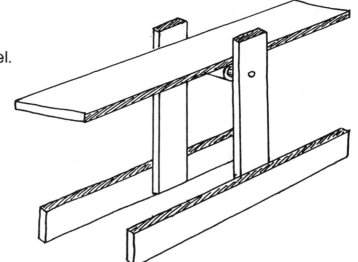

Equipment needed:

junior hacksaw	strip wood
felt pen barrels	glue
5mm dowel	paints
drill with 4mm drill bit	
low melt [cool] glue gun	
scissors	

How to make the example:

Step 1.   Photocopy the sheet opposite, one per child.
Step 2.   Cut out the shapes along the solid black lines.
Step 3.   Stick shapes A, B, C, D and E onto strip wood.
Step 4.   Cut the strip wood to the lengths of the shapes.
Step 5.   Place the shape F next to a felt pen barrel and cut the plastic barrel to the length of the pattern using a junior hacksaw and either a vice or a bench hook.
Step 6.   Glue this piece of felt pen barrel [F] in the position marked on A using a low melt [cool] glue gun. It should stick out either side of the strip wood.
Step 7.   Place G next to a piece of 5mm dowel and cut the dowel to the length of the pattern again using a junior hacksaw and either a vice or a bench hook.
Step 8.   Push G through the section of felt pen barrel attached to A.
Step 9.   Drill through the black dots marked on B and C and push these onto the ends of the dowel creating the legs of the see - saw.
Step 10.   Glue B and C onto D and E where indicated using a low melt [cool] glue gun. D and E will form a stable base for the see - saw.
Step 11.   Glue the bases D and E to the large base which has been glued to thick card.
Step 12.   Test the model and decorate.

How the idea may be developed:

The top of the see - saw could be made from a strip of corrugated plastic and seats could be added.
A group of pupils could create a multiple see - saw.
Model or card figures could be made and added to each end of the see-saw.

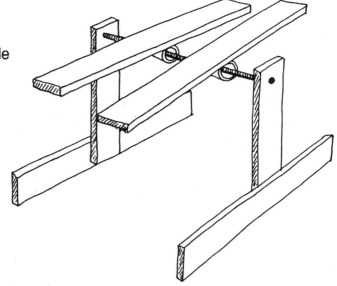

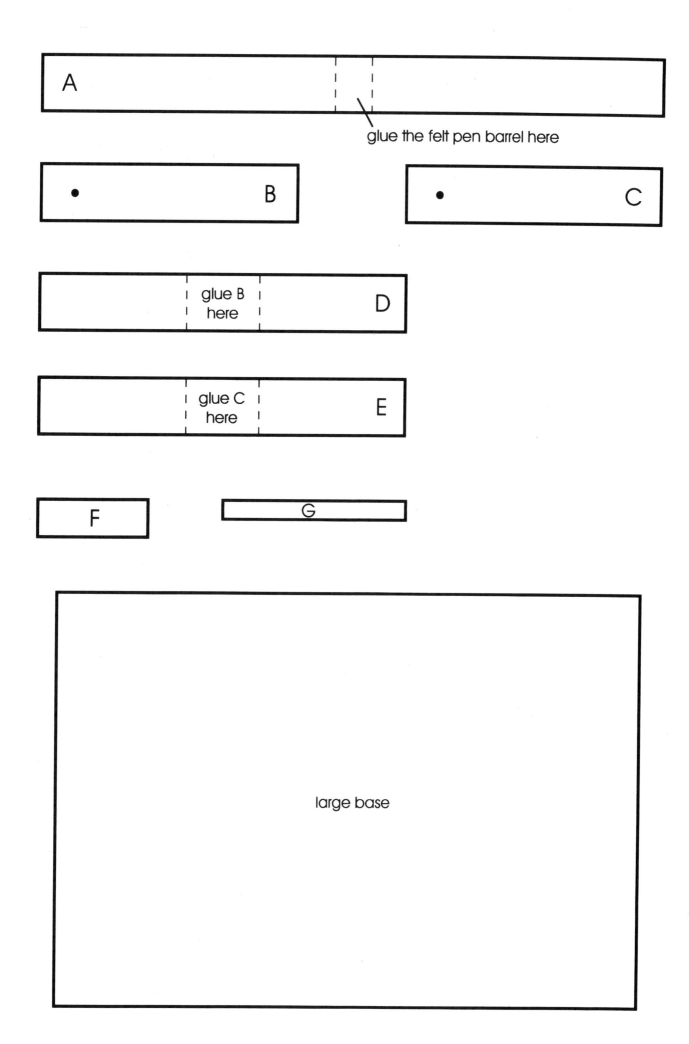

A

glue the felt pen barrel here

B

C

glue B here   D

glue C here   E

F

G

large base

Playground Roundabout

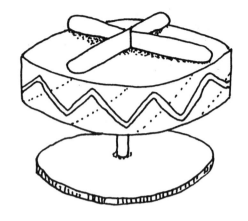

Technique used:

Cotton Reel and fixed dowel.

Equipment needed:

5mm dowel	block of wood
junior hacksaw	lolly sticks
bench hook	cotton reel
wooden wheel	utility snips
low melt [cool] glue gun	
glue	

How to make the example:

Step 1. Photocopy the sheet opposite onto card, one per child.
Step 2. Cut out A along the solid black line to form the top of the roundabout and glue onto thick card.
Step 3. Cut out B along the solid black line, this will form the sides of the roundabout.
Step 4. Decorate B and make into a cylinder by glueing the end tabs together, fold inwards along the dotted lines.
Step 5. Glue the circle A onto the top tabs of the cylinder made from B.
Step 6. Cut 2 lolly sticks in half using the utility snips and glue onto the top circle of the roundabout forming a cross pattern as in the diagram.

Step 7. Cut out C along the solid black line and glue the shape to a piece of thick cardboard or draw around it on a piece of thick card.
Step 8. Cut a piece of dowel 4cm long and push one end into a wooden wheel ensuring a tight fit.
Step 9. Glue the wheel onto the card base made using the template C.
Step 10. Use a low melt [cool] glue gun to stick a cotton reel to the underside of the top of the roundabout.
Step 11. Place the centre hole of the cotton reel over the fixed dowel and test the roundabout.

How the idea may be developed:

A taller roundabout can be made by lengthening the dowel and glueing 2 cotton reels on top of one another on the underside of the roundabout top. Using a drill with a 4mm drill bit, a hole could be drilled in the centre of a 2cm thick wooden base instead of the wheel and the card base. Roundabouts can be made from reclaimed materials e.g. felt pen barrels, cylinders etc.

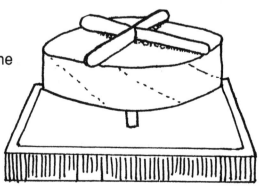

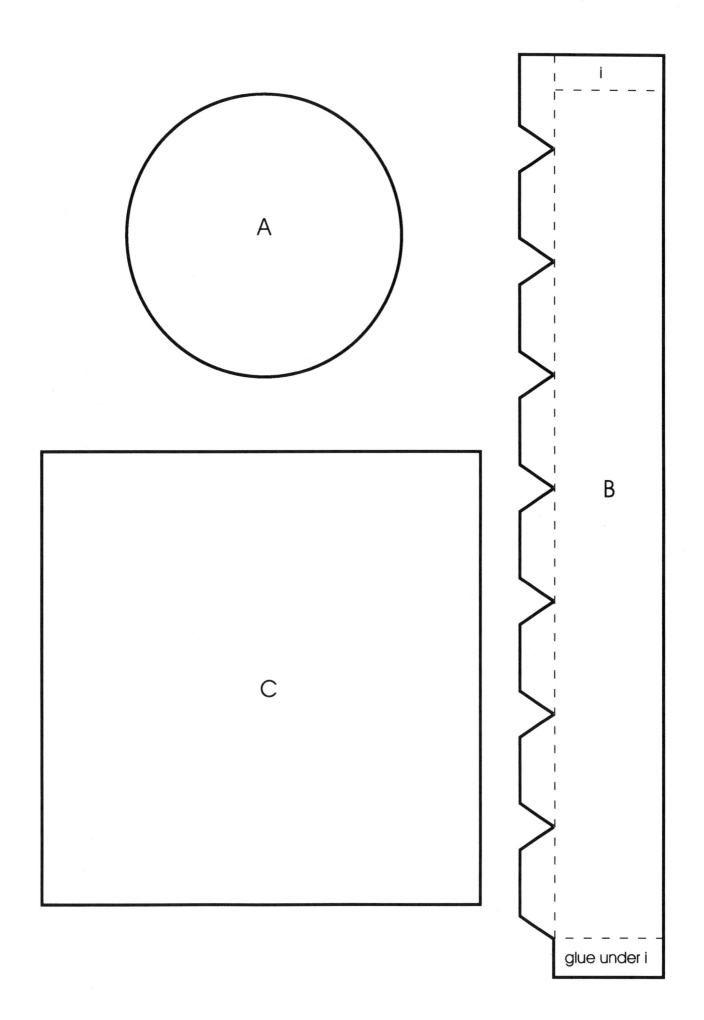

A

B

C

i

glue under i

Swingball Game

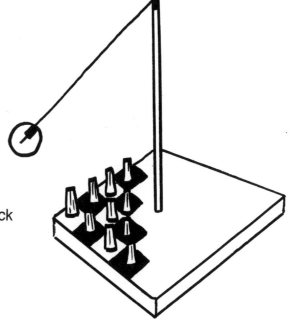

Technique used:

Drilled hole for tight fit dowel.

Equipment needed:

5mm dowel
10 old felt pen lids
low melt [cool] glue gun
plasticine
junior hacksaw
sticky tape
drill with 4mm drill bit

piece of wood
 15cm x 15cm x 1cm thick

string
bench hook
table tennis ball

How to make the example:

Step 1. Photocopy the sheet opposite, one per child.
Step 2. Cut out the chequered square and stick onto the 15cm square piece of wood.
Step 3. Drill a hole in the centre of the 'X'.
Step 4. Cut a piece of 5mm dowel to the length of the pattern on the photocopied sheet.
Step 5. Push the dowel into the drilled hole.
Step 6. Cut a length of string 23 cm long.
Step 7. Stick one end of the string to the table tennis ball using sticky tape.
Step 8. Stick the other end of the string to the top of the dowel in the board.
Step 9. Fill the felt tip pen lids with plasticine to weight them, these will be the skittles.
Step 10. Stand the skittles on the black and white squares, lift the ball and let it swing. How many skittles can the players knock down?

How the idea may be developed:
The pupils could lengthen the dowel and string and see the effect on the swinging of the ball.
Different designs can be made for standing the skittles on. Maybe a game could be created with scores placed on the board.
A large bead or a ball of plasticine could be used instead of a table tennis ball.

X

Spinning Tops

Tight fit dowel.

Equipment needed:

thick card   pencil sharpener
safety snips
5mm dowel
wooden wheels with 4mm drilled centre holes
(or card wheels with 4mm punched hole)

How to make the example:

Step 1.   Photocopy the sheet opposite, one per child.
Step 2.   Cut out the shapes around the solid black lines.
Step 3.   Decorate the patterns for the spinning tops.
Step 4.   Using a junior hacksaw and a bench hook, cut a 7cm length of dowel.
           Sharpen one end using a pencil sharpener.
Step 5.   Glue the decorated spinning tops to circles of card.
Step 6.   Push the sharpened dowel, the spindle, through the centre of the spinning
           top.
Step 7.   Spin the spinning top to see how it works.
Step 8.   Experiment with the other decorated circles to see which:
           i] spin the longest,
           ii] create the most pleasing patterns whilst spinning.

How the idea may be developed:

The pupils can create their own patterns for spinning tops.
Experiment with the length of the spindle. Does the length of the spindle make any
difference to the performance of the spinning top?
Does the surface it spins on make any difference?
Is the size of the card important?
The pupils could decorate wooden or MDF wheels to create their spinning tops. Does
the thickness of the top make any difference to its performance?

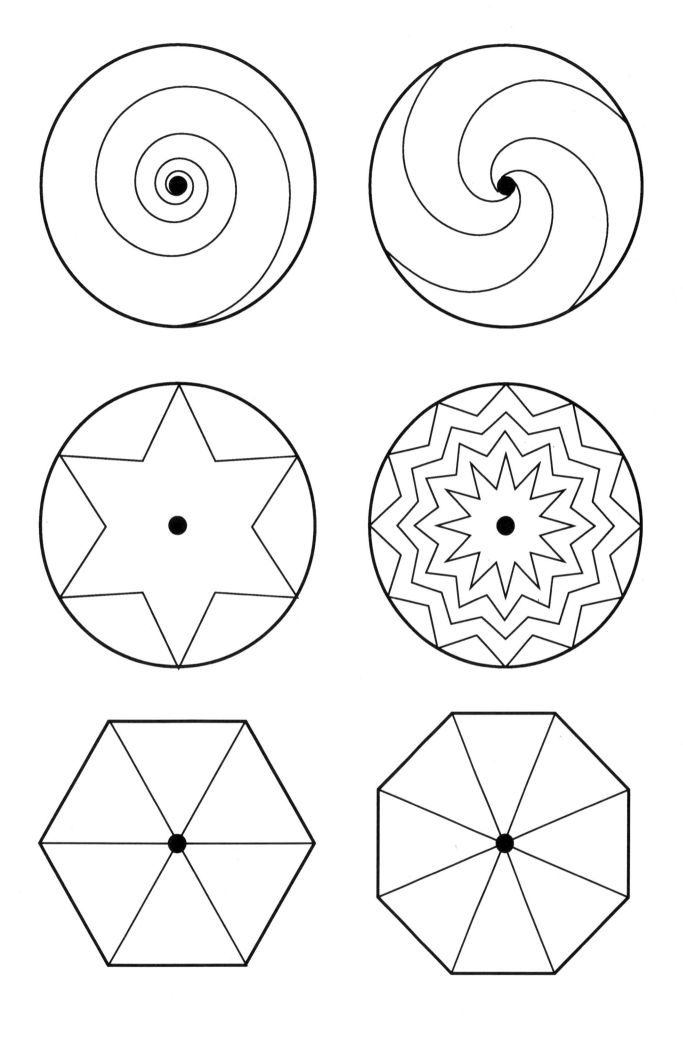

Fishing Game

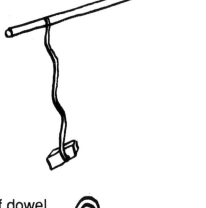

Technique used:

Movement with Magnets

Equipment needed:

2 small magnets
2 x 30cm pieces of string
white card
felt pens

6 large paper clips
2 x 27cm pieces of dowel
sticky tape

How to make the example:

Step 1.   Photocopy the sheet opposite, one per child.

Step 2.   Decorate the fish shapes and cut them out.

Step 3.   Draw around the fish shape onto a piece of card. Cut out the fish shapes and glue the decorated fish onto the thicker card, slide a paper clip onto each fish.

Step 4.   Attach a magnet to the end of each piece of string by glueing or tying.

Step 5.   Attach the other end of the pieces of string to the dowel using sticky tape. Make sure that when attached the strings are the same length to make the game a fair one.

Step 6.   Cut out the 2 pieces of illustrated paper from the photocopied sheet, glue the 2 pieces together as instructed and decorate - these will become the 'pool' sides into whose centre the decorated fish will be placed.

Step 7.   Make the decorated panel into a cylinder and attach the 2 ends with paper clips. In this way when the game is stored, the paper clips can be removed and the 'pool' stored flat.

Step 8.   Place the fish in the centre of the 'pool' and see who can pick up the most fish using the magnet hook on the fishing line.

How the idea may be developed:

The fish could be numbered so that scores can be added up at the end of the game.
The fish shapes can be cut out of foil and the paper clips attached so that the fishing game can be carried out in a bowl of water.
Cork boats can be made as the ones in the picture, and by floating them in a shallow tray of water they can be made to race across the tray by the players holding a stick with a magnet under the tray.

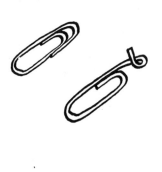

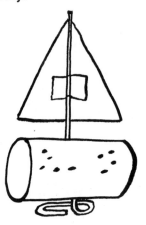

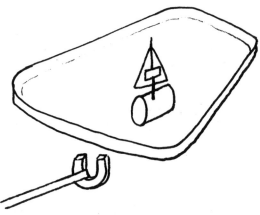

A

glue behind A

31

A Model Tanker

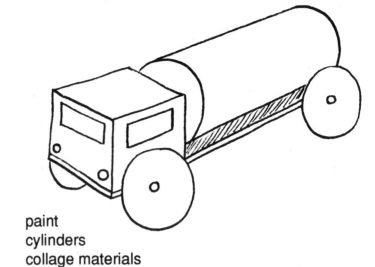

Technique used:

Screw eyes and free moving dowel

Equipment needed:

bradawl
screw eyes
5mm dowel
4mm drilled wheels
teacher prepared wooden bases
boxes - a variety of shapes and sizes
plastic pop bottles
low melt [cool] glue gun

paint
cylinders
collage materials

bench hook
junior hacksaw

How to make the example:

Step 1.   The pupils must choose a piece of wood from a selection of teacher prepared bases. [approx. 10cm x 30cm x 1cm]
Step 2.   Show the pupils some pictures of tankers and a collection of bottles, cylinders and boxes.
Step 3.   The pupils should sort the reclaimed materials into containers suitable for the front cab of the tanker and containers suitable for the tanker part of the model.
Step 4.   The pupils should choose from the containers a box, or boxes suitable for the cab and a bottle or cylinder for the tank.
Step 5.   The teacher should glue these pieces, using a low melt [cool] glue gun, onto the base in the position the pupil describes.
Step 6.   The pupils should make 4 dots with a pencil or felt pen on the base of the vehicle in the position for the screw eyes and with help from the teacher holes must be made with the bradawl over the dots.
Step 7.   Screw the eyes into the holes made with a bradawl.
Step 8.   The pupils should measure the dowel to the correct size and cut to the length required using a bench hook and junior hacksaw.
Step 9.   Push the dowel through the holes in the screw eyes and push wheels onto the ends of the dowel. The wheels will be a tight fit.
Step 10. Decorate the vehicle.

How the idea may be developed:

The pupils can bring vehicles from home to make a display in the classroom.
Pictures of vehicles can be cut out of magazines to create a class, group or individual collage.
The pupils could make the model in a group rather than individually.
The bottles and cylinders can be covered with paper prior to being stuck on the base as this will enable them to be decorated easier.

Equipment List for Key Stage 1

Low melt [cool] glue gun
These operate at a lower temperature than the traditional hot glue gun and although the glue is hot it should not burn the skin. However, it must be used under close supervision. It forms a secure bond when used to join plastics and wood.

Safety Snips

A useful tool for cutting a variety of reclaimed materials and thick card.

Click Rivets
Two part fasteners for attaching card wheels to corrugated plastic. A 5mm hole needs to be made in the wheel first.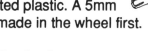

Bradawl

Although sharp, a bradawl is the correct piece of equipment for making small holes in card and plastics.

Utility Snips
These are scissor action and will cut heavy cardboard, thin metal and corrugated plastic.

Wheels

A variety of wheels can be supplied to ensure pupil choice. These can be made of wood or medium density fibreboard [mdf] yet all should have 4mm holes in the centre.

Strip Wood
This can be used for a variety of models and is suitable for drilling.

Circle Cutter

Protect table tops and floors when using this piece of equipment as it contains a sharp blade. It will cut circles up to 35 cm in diameter out of thick card and plastic.

Square Section Wood.
This can be obtained in 8 mm and 10mm size and has a variety of uses.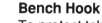

5mm Dowel

This is designed to be a tight fit when used with wheels with a 4mm drilled centre hole.

Corrugated Plastic
A sheet material that can be obtained in 3 mm and 4mm thickness. The corrugated plastic can be cut using a craft knife, safety snips or utility snips and can be hinged by half cutting through the channels.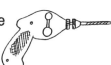

Junior Hacksaw

Strong pistol grip hacksaws are safe to use and blades are easily changed.

Drill
A pistol grip drill is very easy to use and drill bits on most models, can be stored in the handles.

Wooden bases

These should be prepared by adults in varying shapes and sizes and between 1 cm and 2 cm thick.

Hammer
Small, lightweight hammers can be used with small nails or panel pins as in cable clips.

Vice

Young children should hold their wood in a vice when cutting. When using a hand drill, the object to be drilled should be held in a vice.

Pliers
A useful tool for gripping and bending wire and paper clips.

Round File

A useful piece of equipment for increasing the size of holes and for smoothing drilled holes and sharp edges.

Bench Hook
To protect tables when cutting square sectioned wood, strip wood and dowel. They are usually suitable for both left and right handed pupils and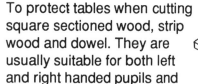

Construction Techniques for Key Stage 2

Paper Clips and Free Moving Dowel

Paper clips can easily be bent to an angle of 90° using a pair of pliers. The curved ends of the paper clips will then allow a piece of 5mm dowel to move freely through them and the paper clips can be attached to wood, plastic or card using a low melt [cool] glue gun.

Loose and Tight Fit Dowel

Ready drilled wheels with a 4mm centre hole are a tight fit on 5mm dowel. If however you require a wheel to be free moving on a piece of dowel then the hole in the centre of the wheel needs to be enlarged and this can be done by re - drilling the wheel with a drill fitted with a 6mm drill bit.

Felt Pen Barrels and Free Moving Dowel

The plastic barrels from felt pens are very useful items and once felt tips run out, the barrels should be washed and saved. The barrels allow dowel to move freely through them.

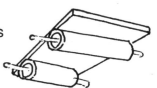

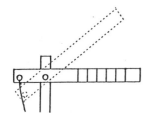

Levers

A versatile way of gaining movement in toys and models made from card and corrugated plastic. The close links with science should be emphasised. A lever is a bar / rod that pivots around a fixed point. When one part of the bar is moved the other side moves side moves also often in a different direction, only the fixed point stays in the same place.
Linkages are 2 or more levers joined together.

Offset Hole Cam

Because the hole in the wheel is not in the centre, as the wheel moves along it moves up and down acting as a cam.

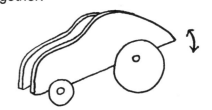

Pulleys

A pulley is a grooved wheel for a driving belt to pass over and is used for transferring power. A cotton reel fixed on a shaft and moved by a belt, in this case an elastic band, can be used to do this.

Strip and Dowel Chassis

A versatile construction technique that forms a rigid structure without the use of adhesives.

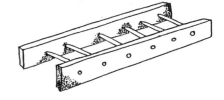

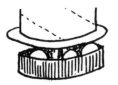

Marble Bearings

A useful way of introducing simple bearings to pupils. This can be linked to a science topic on Forces and a number of bearings tested along with surfaces and weight and how these relate to friction and speed in the toys and models.

Card Triangles

Square section and strip wood can be fastened at 90' angles by using card triangles glued to the top and bottom surfaces of the wood. These form a suprisingly strong structure that is useful for creating a frame.

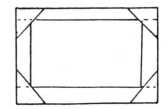

Pneumatics

Models can be made by using air as a force- pneumatics. Syringes are a cheap and effective way of compressing air to use in pneumatics.

Equipment List for Key Stage 2

Besides the equipment listed below, the pupils should be instructed in the safe and correct way of using all the equipment from the Key Stage 1 list.

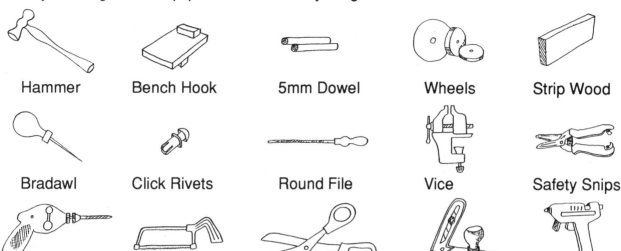

Hammer   Bench Hook   5mm Dowel   Wheels   Strip Wood

Bradawl   Click Rivets   Round File   Vice   Safety Snips

Drill   Junior Hacksaw   Utility Snips   Circle Cutter   Glue Gun

Metal Safety Ruler
An essential piece of equipment if craft knives are to be used as it keeps the pupils fingers out of the way!

Craft Knife
Only use knives with retractable blades. Use in conjunction with a cutting mat and local safety regulations.

Motors
Small, cheap and reliable electric motors should be used on Key Stage 2 pupils models. They are operated by one battery.

Bulbs
1.5v and 2.5v bulbs can be operated by one battery and should be connected to a bulb holder.

Small Pulley
These can be attached directly onto the shaft of a motor and ensure rubber bands work correctly to power models.

Wire Cutter and Stripper
This tool cuts wire and automatically strips away plastic insulation leaving the bare wire exposed for reliable connections.

Cylinders
A collection of cylinders in a wide range of sizes and materials should be made available as these are useful materials for avariety of models

Card Triangles
These can be used to join square section and strip wood to create lightweight chassis and structures

Roman Chariot

Technique used:

Paper clips and free moving dowel.

Equipment needed:

thick card pliers
safety snips card
paper clips glue
5mm dowel hole punch
wheels with 4mm drilled centre holes
low melt [cool] glue gun

How to make the example:

Step 1.   Photocopy the sheet opposite, one per child.
Step 2.   Cut out the shapes around the solid black lines.
Step 3.   Stick the base template onto thick card and cut the thick card to the shape of the base pattern.
Step 4.   Hold one end of a paper clip with pliers and bend the other end to an angle of 90°
Step 5.   Glue one of the ends of the bent paper clip onto the top of the base in the positions indicated on the pattern. Repeat the process with the other side.

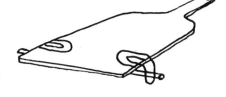

Step 6.   Decorate the side panel of the chariot and fold along the dotted lines inwards.
Step 7.   Glue the side panel onto the base in the position indicated on the pattern.
Step 8.   Make a hole through the black dot on the base.
Step 9.   Cut a length of 5mm dowel 10cm long.
Step 10. Push the dowel through the paper clips and attach wheels to the ends.

How the idea may be developed:
The pupils should make patterns for their own designs of chariot bases, these should be symmetrical and should be displayed with the finished models to show the pupils' involvement in the Design process.
Horses to pull the chariots can be created out of mouldable or reclaimed materials and construction kits.

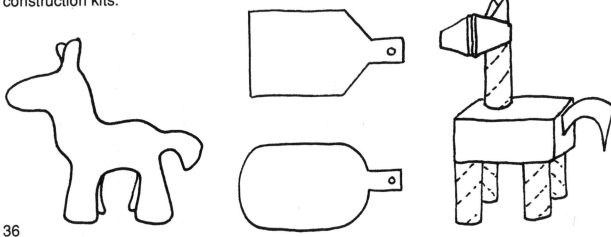

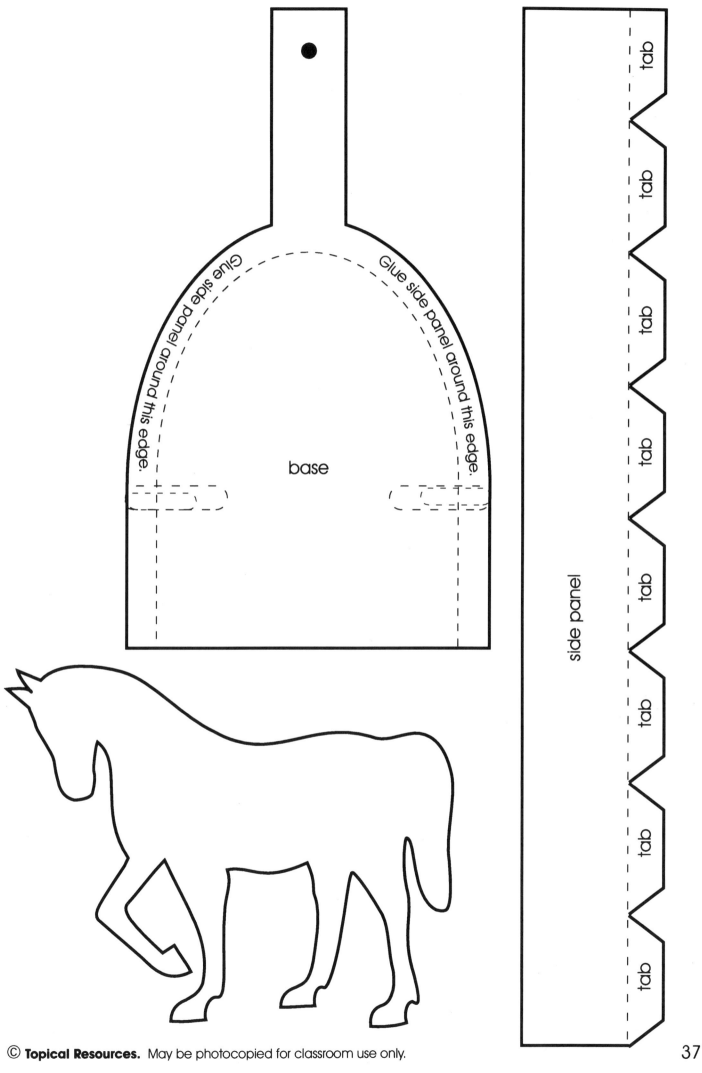

base

Glue side panel around this edge.

Glue side panel around this edge.

side panel

tab tab tab tab tab tab tab tab tab

37

Bouncing Car

Technique used:

Offset Hole Cam.

Equipment needed:

glue	5mm dowel
junior hacksaw	bench hook
felt pens	drill with 4mm drill bit
wooden or mdf wheels	
single hole punch or paper drill	

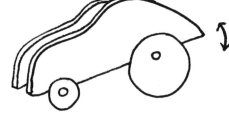

How to make the example:

Step 1.   Photocopy the sheet opposite onto card or paste onto card, one per child.
Step 2.   Cut out the net and the car sides along the thick black lines.
Step 3.   Fold along the dotted lines drawn on the net and make the cuboid.
Step 4.   Decorate the car side panels.
Step 5.   Using a single hole punch or a paper drill, make 4 holes through the black dots, 2 on each side of the car. Make sure that the holes are large enough for the dowel to be free moving through them.
Step 6.   Using the bench hook and junior hacksaw, cut 2 pieces of 5mm dowel which are 5 cms long.
Step 7.   Glue the net onto the back of one of the car side panels as in the diagram.
Step 8.   Glue the back of the second part of the car to the opposite side of the net ensuring the punched holes on the right and left side are lined up with each other.
Step 9.   Push one piece of dowel through the front holes and attach wheels to each end of the axle. The wheels will be a tight fit on the axle.
Step 10.   Take two wheels and using the drill fitted with a 4mm bit, drill the wheels off centre together to ensure that they are re - drilled in the same position, as in the digram.
This forms an offset hole cam because the hole is not in the centre. The wheel moves up and down as it turns and this makes it act as a cam.
Step 11.   Push the other piece of dowel through the back holes on the car and attach the re - driilled wheels to this axle through the new offset holes.
Step 12.   Test the vehicle.

How the idea may be developed:

This mechanism can be used on any wheels which are attached to a variety of models made by the pupils.
Experiment with altering the position of the offset cam, will this make any difference to the way in which the cam will work? Pupils could make their own vehicle designs.

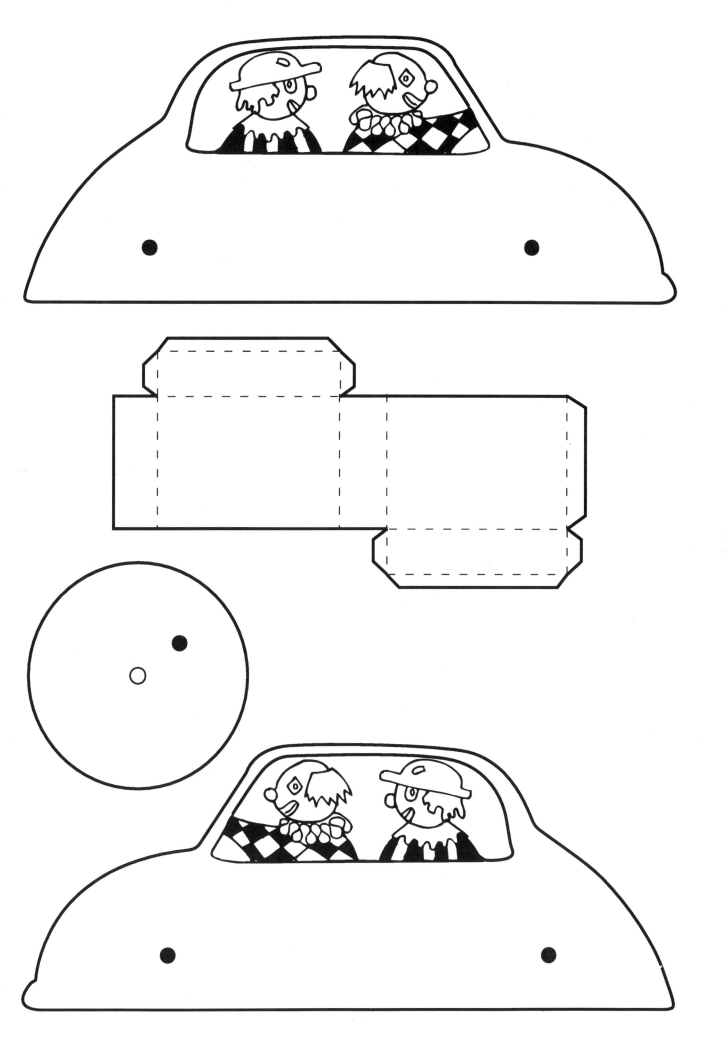

Turning Butterflies

Technique used:

Pulleys

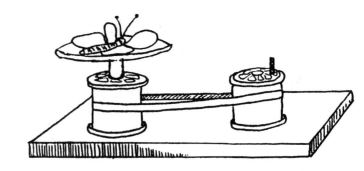

Equipment needed:

cotton reels	5mm dowel
wooden bases	glue
elastic bands	plastic tubing
drill fitted with 4mm drill bit	

How to make the example:

Step 1. Photocopy the sheet opposite onto card, one per child.
Step 2. Cut out the shapes.
Step 3. Cut out the 2 centre circle shapes from the base plate template.
Step 4. Glue the base template onto a piece of wood which can be slightly larger than the pattern. Decorate the pattern.
Step 5. Drill into the centre of the cut out circles.
Step 6. Cut 2 pieces of dowel which are 3cm long.
Step 7. Push the 2 pieces of dowel into the drilled holes. This should be a tight fit.
Step 8. Place the central hole of a cotton reel over each piece of dowel.
Step 9. Select an elastic band that fits snugly around the 2 cotton reels as in the diagram.
Step 10. Decorate the butterfly and glue onto the top of the cotton reel on the left hand side of the base.
Step 11. Cut a piece of dowel 4cm in length.
Step 12. Push the piece of dowel into a small piece of plastic tubing.
Step 13. Push the end of the dowel encased in plastic tubing into one of the top triangular sections of the cotton reel on the right hand side of the base, this will form the handle.
Step 14. Turn the handle clockwise and the butterfly will turn.

How the idea may be developed:

Experiment with the mechanism. Try turning the handle anti-clockwise. Does the butterfly turn at the same speed as the handle pulley?

If a cross over is placed in the elastic band will the mechanism still work?

Make a roundabout from recycled materials and add it to the top of one of the cotton reels to create a fairground ride.

Add a third shaft and cotton reel to the system. How will this effect the mechanism?

Combine the pulleys with the techniques for making a vehicle chassis and create a vehicle with a crane.

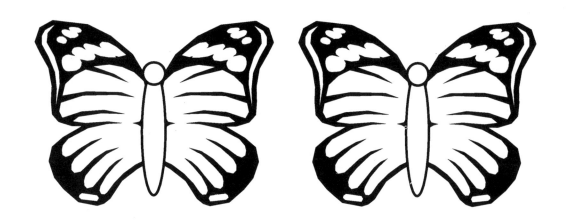

Spinning Roundabout.

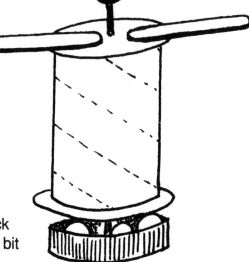

Technique used:

Marble Bearings.

Equipment needed:

marbles	5mm dowel
glue	junior hacksaw
bench hook	2 wheels
low melt, cool glue gun	lolly sticks
bead	safety snips
piece of wood approx.12cms square and 1 cm thick	
drill with 4mm drill bit	drill with 6mm drill bit

How to make the example:

Step 1.   Photocopy the sheet opposite, one per child.

Step 2.   Cut out the three shapes around the thick black lines.

Step 3.   Decorate the shape with diagonal lines to create the wrapping for the central column. Stick it around the central tubing from a toilet or kitchen roll which is 12 cms in length.

Step 4.   Stick the circle onto thick card and using safety snips cut the thick card to the same size as the circle.

Step 5.   Stick the rectangular piece of card with tabs onto the base as directed and this will form a shallow circular tray to hold the marble bearings.

Step 6.   Drill a 4mm hole in the centre of the piece of wood and also in the centre of the shallow circular tray.

Step 7.   Glue the tray onto the top of the piece of wood ensuring the holes are lined up.

Step 8.   Cut a piece of dowel 20cms in length and push it into the drilled hole. It must be a tight fit.

Step 9.   Re - drill the centres of two wheels with the 6mm drill bit and then glue them onto the 2 ends of the covered cylinder.

Step 10. Place 6 marbles in the shallow tray.

Step 11. Place the holes in the wheels on the column over the piece of dowel, as in the diagram. Ensure the column is free moving.

Step12. Glue 2 lolly sticks onto the top of the column as in the diagram and a bead to the top of the piece of dowel. Test your model.

How the idea may be developed:

The model can be decorated in many different ways.
Try creating a figure from the basic construction.
Test the models performance by adding more marbles to the tray or by removing marbles. What are the fewest number of marbles that can act as bearings?
A coffee jar lid may be used instead of making your own circular tray to hold the marbles.

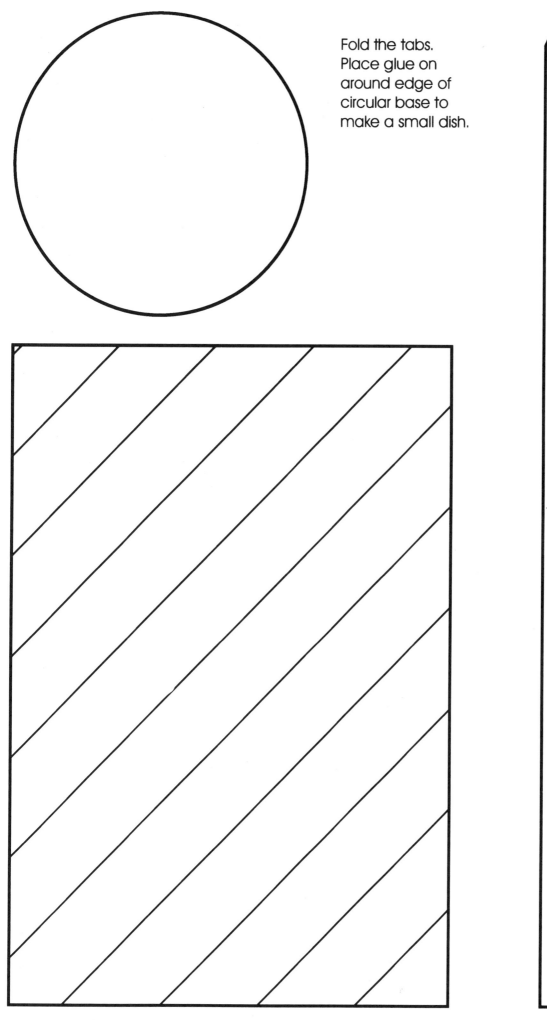

Fold the tabs.
Place glue on
around edge of
circular base to
make a small dish.

tab

tab
tab
tab
tab
tab
tab
tab
tab
tab
tab
tab
tab
tab

tab

Rotating Windmill

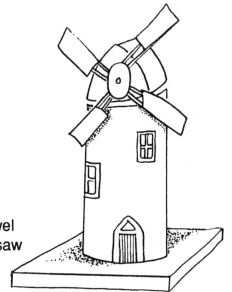

Technique used:

Loose and tight fit dowel

Equipment needed:

low melt, cool glue gun	card
cardboard tube	5mm dowel
wooden or mdf wheels	bench hook
4mm & 6mm drill bit	beads to fit dowel
wooden base, approx. 1cm thick	drill & jun. hacksaw

How to make the example:

Step 1. Photocopy the sheet opposite onto card, one per child.

Step 2. Let the pupils cut out the shapes along the thick black lines and stick the 2 circles onto very thick card which is cut to the same size.

Step 3. Drill a 4mm hole in the centre of the wooden base.

Step 4. Cut a piece of dowel so that it is 25cms in length.

Step 5. Glue the dowel into the drilled hole. It must be a tight fit.

Step 6. Place a card tube measuring 12cms in length over the dowel and glue it onto the base.

Step 7. Place a wooden bead onto the dowel and glue it in position so that it is level with the top of the cardboard cylinder, as in the diagram.

Step 8. Cut 8 pieces of dowel which are 14 cms in length and glue them along the lines drawn on one of the photocopied thick circles. Stick the plain circle on top of the dowel ensuring the circle edges are in line and with the 4mm drill bit, drill through the centre of the card circles.

Step9. Using safety snips, cut sections from a plastic washing up bottle that are equal in size to the 4 card templates. These will form the sails that will be slightly curved.

Step 10. Glue the sails onto the dowel on the concave side so that the sails are curving outwards. The dowel must be glued in the correct position as shown in the diagram.

Step 11. Re - drill 2 wheels with the 6mm drill bit.

Step 12. Cut a section of dowel 6cms in length and glue the end into the tight fit hole drilled in the centre of the card circles.

Step 13. Glue the other end of the dowel onto one of the re - drilled wheels as in the diagram. Glue the second re - drilled wheel on top of the dowel.

Step 14. Slide the re - drilled wheels, which will be a loose fit, over the central dowel and glue a bead on the top of these leaving space for the wheels to spin freely.

How the idea may be developed:

The pupils must test their model and make a top for their windmill.

Would the windmill work as well with more or fewer sails or with sails of a different size or shape?

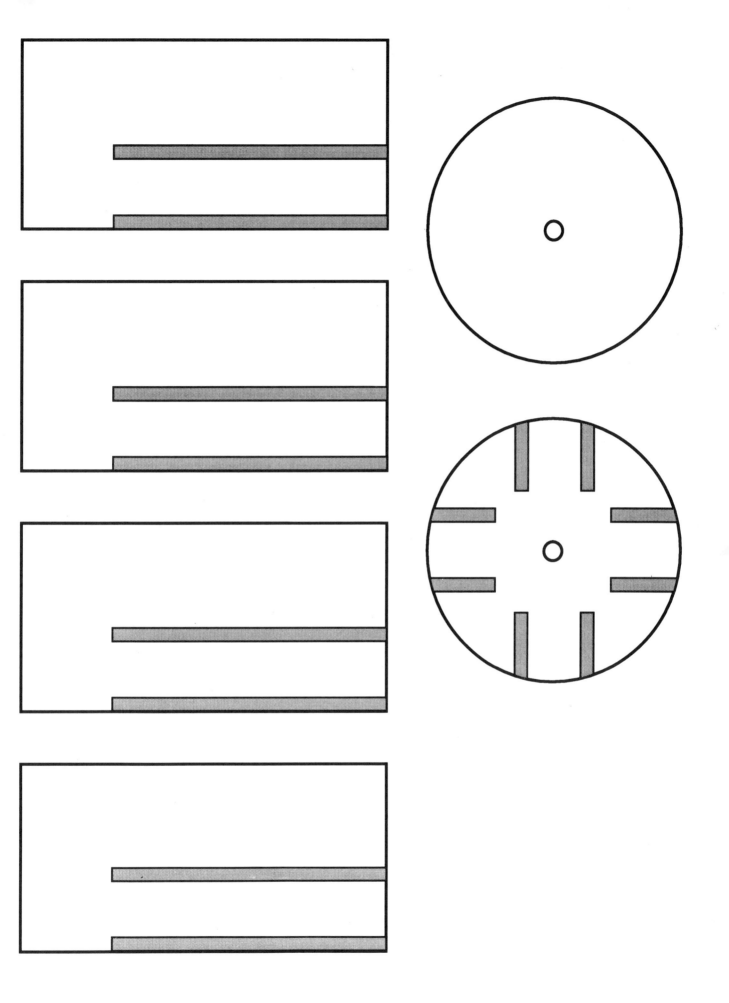

High Speed Wind Turbine

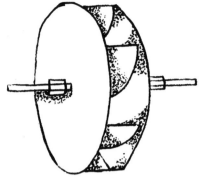

Technique used:

Loose fit dowel

Equipment needed:

low melt, cool glue gun
4mm dowel
pva
plastic tubing

card
scissors
paper drill

How to make the example:

Step 1.   Photocopy the sheet opposite onto card or paste onto card, one per child.
Step 2.   Let the pupils cut out the shapes for the side plates and the blades of their turbine.
Step 3.   Using a paper drill make a hole in the centre of the two side plates where indicated by the black dots.
Step 4.   Carefully glue the turbine blades into position on the curved lines with pva or a low melt, cool glue gun.
Step 5.   Put glue along the top edges of the turbine blades and carefully place the second side plate in position taking care to line up the edges of the circles.
Step 6.   Cut a piece of dowel 30cms in length.
Step 7.   Push the dowel through the holes in the side plates, it must be a loose fit. If the turbine does not move freely on the dowel, remove the dowel and carefully enlarge the holes with a round file. Replace the dowel.
Step 8.   To stop the turbine falling off the shaft, push a small section of plastic tubing over each end of the dowel and move it close to the sides of the turbine.
Step 9.   Hold the dowel at each end and blow across the top of the turbine.
Step 10.   Test your turbine:

a) Blow across the top and the bottom. Which way does it move the fastest?
b) How slow can your turbine turn?
c) How fast can it move?

How the idea may be developed:

Does the size or shape of the blades
affect the movement?
Can other materials be used?
How can this technique be used to power a model?

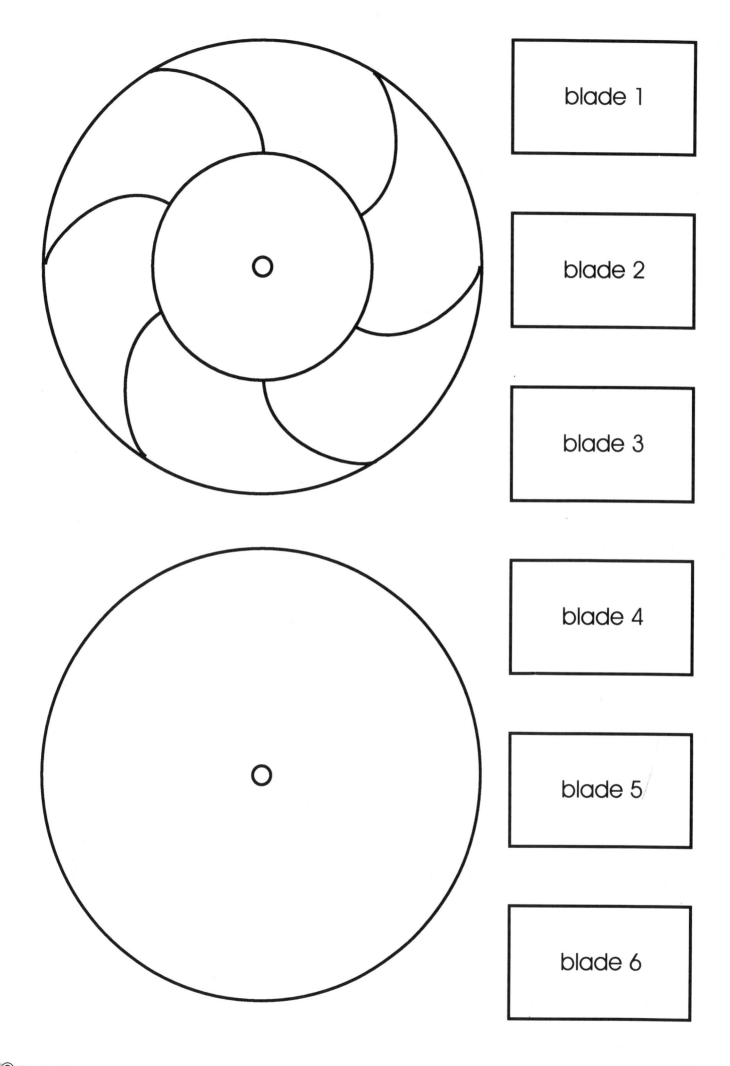

blade 1

blade 2

blade 3

blade 4

blade 5

blade 6

47

Hovercraft

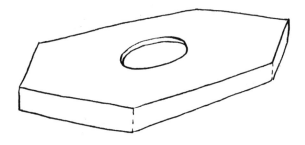

Technique used:

Folding and scoring

Equipment needed:

Pritt Stick or similar   card
hair drier
scissors

How to make the example:

Step 1. Photocopy the sheet opposite onto card for use as a template, one per child.
Step 2. Let the pupils cut out the base shape of their hovercraft and the centre hole.
Step 3. Make sure all the solid black lines are cut.
Step 4. Score the dotted lines using scissors.
Step 5. Bend the outer edges in at the fold marks to make the skirt.
Step 6. Glue the tabs to seal all the gaps.
Step 7. Test the vehicle by:
      a) blowing down the central hole
      b) blowing the column of air from a hair drier down the central hole.
      N.B. Never use a hair dryer near water.

How the idea may be developed:

The pupils can vary: base shapes, length of
skirt, size of hole, strength of hairdrier,
different types of material etc to see how
performance changes.
Construct a paper tube to direct the air
into the hole. Does this improve the design?
Try different cabin shapes.
Try the hovercraft on different surfaces -
on which does it perform best?
Can ready made objects such as reclaimed
fish and chip trays be used to make
model hovercraft?

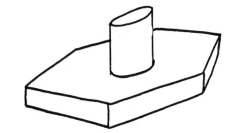

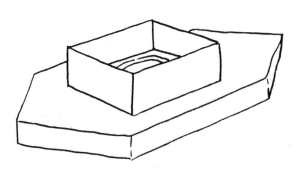

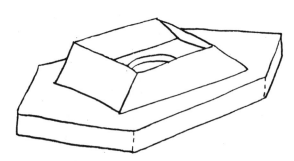

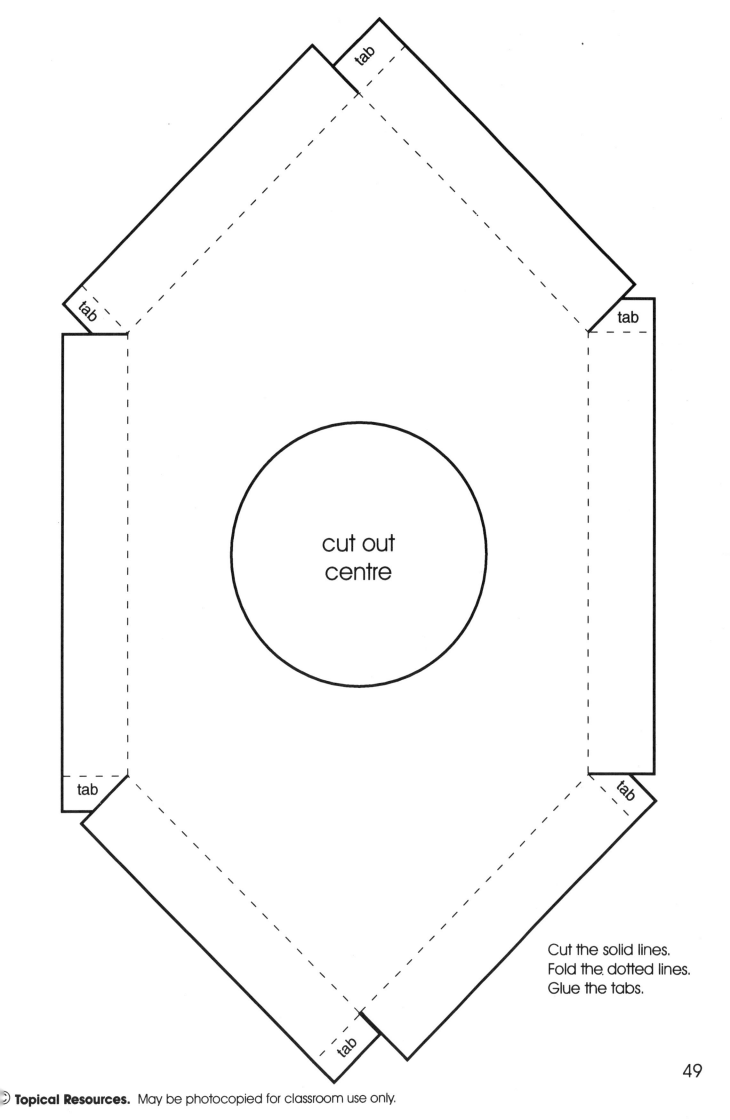

tab

tab

tab

tab

tab

tab

cut out
centre

Cut the solid lines.
Fold the dotted lines.
Glue the tabs.

49

Paddle Boat

Technique used:

Elastic band power

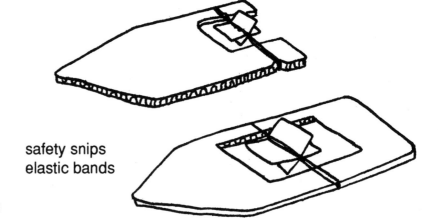

Equipment needed:

corrugated plastic	safety snips
utility snips	elastic bands

How to make the example:

Step 1.   Photocopy the sheet opposite onto card.
Step 2.   Cut out the shapes along the solid black lines.
Step 3.   Use the shapes as templates and draw around them onto corrugated plastic.
Step 4.   Cut out the slots A and B indicated by the dotted lines on the templates.
Step 5.   Fit together the two paddle pieces by sliding the slots together in an interlocking way as shown in the diagram:

Step 6.   Select an elastic band that will fit loosely over the centre cross of the paddle.
Step 7.   Position the paddle in the space at the rear of the base and stretch the elastic band until the loops fit into the notches on each side of the bars.
Step 8.   Wind the paddle approximately 20 times, place the boat on water and release the paddle, watch the paddle boat move.

How the idea may be developed:

The pupils should design their own base shapes for the paddle boat. These must be drawn on paper patterns before being transferred to corrugated plastic and the patterns displayed with the finished models.
Tests should be made to determine whether or not the shape of the base effects the performance of the boat.
Other materials should be tested for their suitability as bases, the results recorded and displayed.
Could the paddle be placed in a different position on the boat?

Experiment with different types of power for the base of your boat.
Could a sail be added and blown to move the boat?
Could the pupils create a 'jet' boat by attaching a balloon to the base. When the air is released from the balloon the force of the escaping air would power the boat forwards.

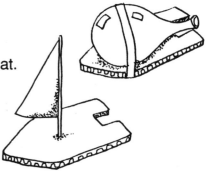

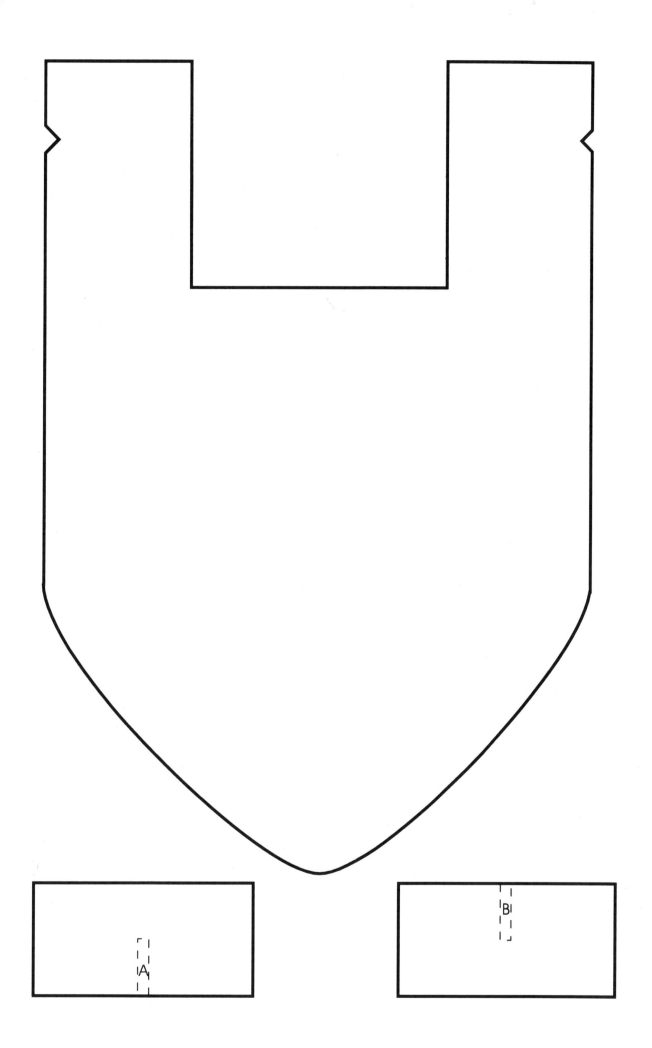

51

Strip Vehicle Chassis

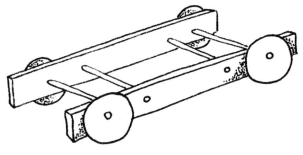

Technique used:

Strip and dowel construction

Equipment needed:

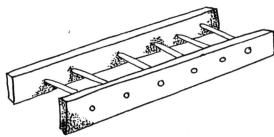

strip wood	5mm dowel
wheels	drill
4mm drill bit	6mm drill bit
narrow round file	junior hacksaw
bench hook	

How to make the example:

Step 1. Photocopy the sheet opposite, one per child.

Step 2. Using the junior hacksaw and bench hook, cut 2 pieces of strip wood which are equal in length to the sides of the chassis on the sheet - 18cms.

Step 3. Fasten the two pieces together using masking tape or elastic bands so that both pieces can be drilled at the same time to ensure the holes are in the same places on both pieces of wood.

Step 4. Mark 2 crosses two and a half cms from the end of the top piece of strip wood as in the diagram.

Step 5. Mark 2 black dots 5cms from the end of the top piece of strip wood as in the diagram.

Step 6. Drill through the centre of the two black crosses with the 6mm drill bit. This will make a loose fit hole to enable the dowel for the axle to move freely.

Step 7. Drill through the centre of the 2 black dots with the 4mm drill bit to ensure a tight fit for the cross fittings on the chassis.

Step 8. Before taking off the masking tape or elastic bands, mark one end of both pieces of wood with small arrows facing each other. This will ensure the correct positioning of the sides of the chassis when fastened with the dowel.

Step 9. Remove the masking tape or elastic bands and separate the two pieces of strip wood.

Step 10 Cut 2 pieces of dowel 9cms long and two pieces of dowel 12 cms long.

Step 11. Place the 2 pieces of 9cms long dowel through the tight fit holes marked 'A' and 'B' on the diagram. This will make a rigid chassis structure and requires no glueing.

Step 12. Push the 2 pieces of 12cms dowel through the loose fit holes marked 'C' and 'D' in the diagram to create the axles. If the axles are not completely free moving then smooth or enlarge the drilled holes by using the round file.

Step 13. Push the wheels onto the ends of the axles. They must be a tight fit.

Step 14. Test the vehicle.

How the idea may be developed.

This is an ideal construction for creating a variety of vehicle bases. The pupils can create the body for the vehicle by using a net or reclaimed materials. Many interesting models can be made in this way. Experiment with a catapult or perhaps a battering ram.

The dimensions written on this diagram are accurate. However, the width of the strip wood used for the chassis sides may vary between 5mm and 10mm depending on the supplier. This will not affect the workings of your model in any way.

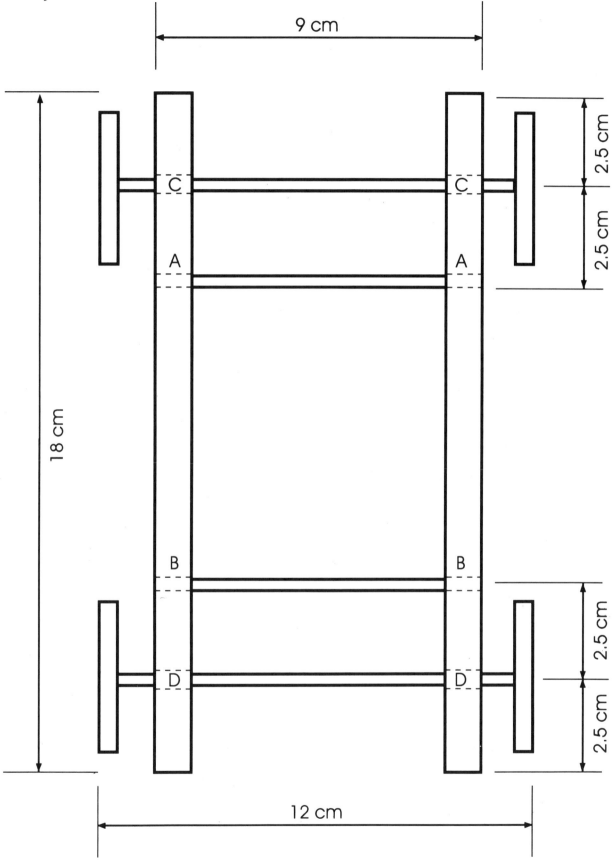

Elastic Band Powered Strip Vehicle Chassis

Technique used:

Strip and dowel construction with elastic band

Equipment needed:

strip wood	5mm dowel
wheels	drill
4mm drill bit	6mm drill bit
round file	junior hacksaw
bench hook	variety of sizes of elastic bands

How to make the example:

Step 1.   Make the strip and dowel chassis as described on the previous page.

Step 2.   Photocopy the sheet opposite onto card or paste onto card, one per child.

Step 3.   Cut out the net around the solid black lines.

Step 4.   Cut down the 4 short solid black lines on the net.

Step 5.   Fold along the dotted lines on the net.

Step 6.   Glue all the tabs marked 'A' behind the sections marked 'B' on the net to form a shallow box.

Step 7.   Place an elastic band under the front chassis dowel. By looking at the chassis diagram the pupils can see that this is marked as 'A'.

Step 8.   Place one end of the elastic band through the loop formed by the other end of the elastic band. This will attach the elastic band securely to the dowel.

Step 9.   Wrap the looped end of the elastic band around the front axle of the vehicle. To wrap the elastc band securely, hold it in place on the axle and wind the wheels to stretch the elastic band.

Step 10.   Place the vehicle on an unpolished surface and release the front axle. The elastic band will unwind and power the vehicle forwards.

Step 11.   Glue the box which has been created onto the elastic band powered vehicle ensuring it is not touching the wheels.

Step 12.   Test your vehicle. It may move better if weights are placed in the box. Experiment.

How the idea may be developed:

The pupils can create the vehicle chassis using their own measurements. It can be as long or as short as they wish and the width can also be changed.
A paddle boat can be made using the same technique, as in the diagram.
What other models can be created using this technique?
e.g cars, buses, trains etc...

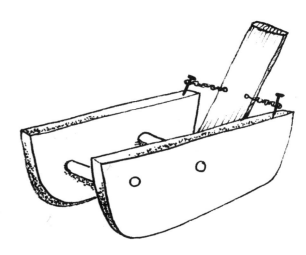

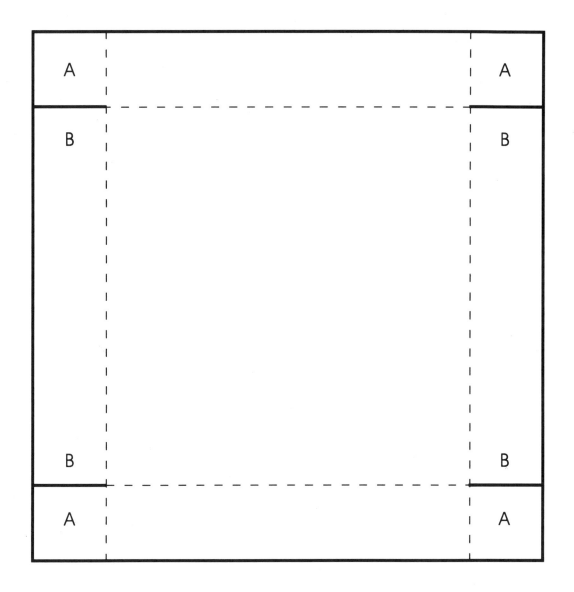

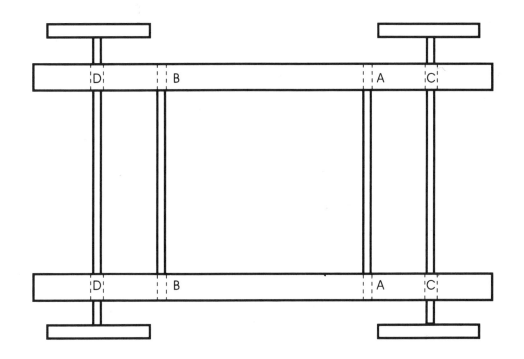

Motorised Strip Vehicle Chassis

Technique used:

Strip and dowel construction with a motor added.

Equipment needed:

strip wood	5mm dowel	wheels
4mm drill bit	6mm drill bit	drill
round file	junior hacksaw	wire
bench hook	motor pulley	motor
masking tape	low melt, cool glue gun	
elastic bands	automatic wire cutter and stripper	

How to make the example:

Step 1.   Photocopy the sheet opposite, one per child.

Step 2.   The pupils should decide upon the size of their strip and dowel chassis and enter the measurements onto the diagram to create an annotated drawing.

Step 3.   Once the measurements have been decided upon then the chassis should be created using the same sequence of construction techniques as described on page 52.

Step 4.   Once the basic chassis construction is completed, test the vehicle.

Step 5.   Cut two pieces of strip wood to the required length so that they fit across the middle of the chassis and are glued to the two side sections as in the diagram.

Step 6.   Using a low melt glue gun, attach the motor to these cross sections with the shaft of the motor positioned opposite the centre of the axle.

Step 7.   To ensure the motor is attached securely, wrap masking tape around the motor and the strip wood.

Step 8.   Push the pulley onto the shaft of the motor.

Step 9.   Cut 2 pieces of wire that each measure one metre in length.

Step 10. Attach one end of each piece of wire to the connections on the motor by twisting.

Step 11. Take off one of the front wheels from the vehicle and remove the axle from one side of the strip wood.

Step 12. Onto this axle place 5 elastic bands of varying lengths. Push the dowel back through the drilled loose fit hole and reattach the wheel.

Step 13. Place one of the elastic bands around the drive shaft on the motor. Hold one end of the wires to the positive end of the battery and one end to the negative end of the battery. The elastic band should move the axle and the vehicle should be powered forwards.

Step 14. If the vehicle does not move, cut off this elastic band and try another one from the range that have been chosen.

Step 15. Once the vehicle moves, reverse movement can be obtained by changing the wires over from positive to negative and visa versa.

How the idea may be developed:

Can more permanent way can be made to connect the wires to the battery? Let the pupils experiment making a switch to control forwards and reverse movement. The pupils can experiment with these techniques to create a cable car or a crane.

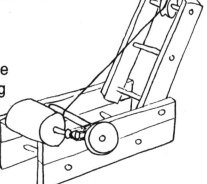

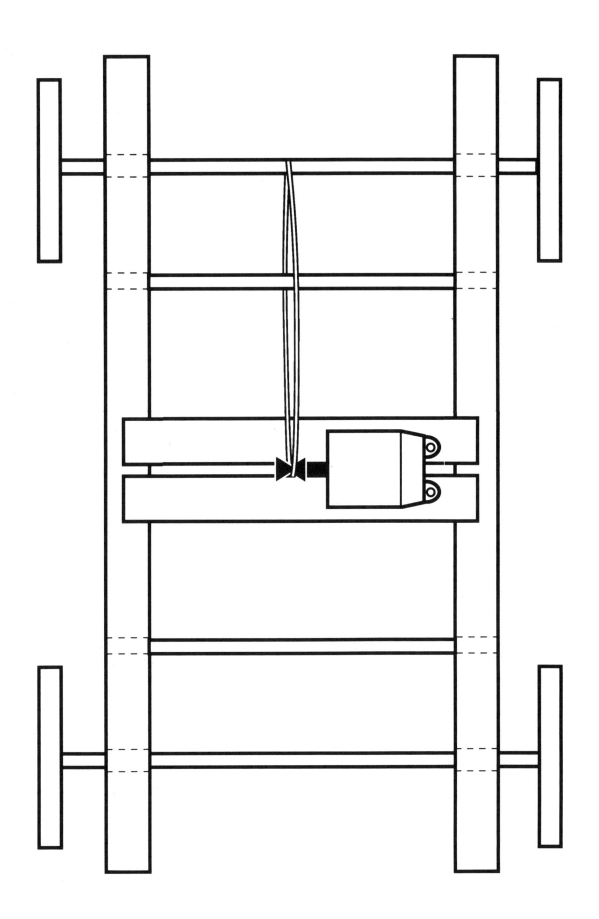

Square Section Wood Vehicle Chassis

Technique used:

Square section wood construction with cardboard triangle corners.

Equipment needed:

10mm square section wood	5mm dowel
6mm drill bit	drill
round file	junior hacksaw
low melt, cool glue gun	wheels - card, wood or mdf
pva glue	

How to make the example:

Step 1.   Photocopy the sheet opposite, one per child.
Step 2.   Cut out the plan for the triangles along the solid black lines and glue it onto card.
Step 3.   Using the junior hacksaw and the bench hook, cut 2 pieces of wood which are 6cms long and 2 pieces of wood which are 15 cms long.
Step 4.   Fasten the two pieces of 15cms wood together using masking tape, as in the diagram and mark two black dots 3 cms away from the ends of the top piece.
Step 5.   Drill through the centres of the black dots.
Step 6.   Remove the masking tape and on a flat surface position the four pieces of strip wood as in the diagram.
Step 7.   Cut four triangles from your photocopied sheet.
Step 8.   Using either pva glue or the low melt glue gun, stick the four triangles over the corners of the wood as in the diagram.
Step 9.   Turn the frame over, cut four more triangles and glue them in place.
Step 10. Cut 2 pieces of 5mm dowel so that they are 11 cms long.
Step 11. When the glue is dry, push the dowel through the holes in the sides of the chassis. If the dowel is not free moving in the holes then the holes must be smoothed or enlarged using the round file.
Step 12. Push wheels onto the ends of the axles.
Step 13. Test the vehicle.

How the idea may be developed:

The pupils can build up the vehicles body using nets or reclaimed materials. This technique can be used to create a picture frame which the pupils can decorate. This construction is light yet strong. Sails could be added to create a land yacht which can be tested in the playground or blown by the pupils or by using a hair drier.

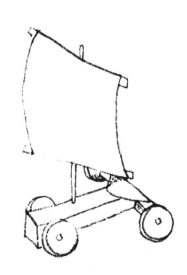

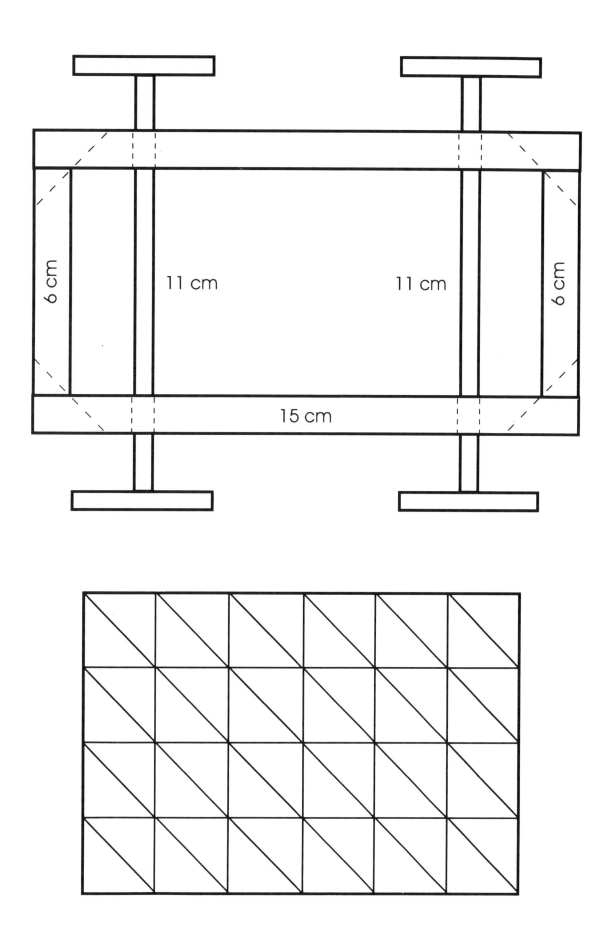

6 cm   11 cm   11 cm   6 cm

15 cm

Clown with Spinning Bow Tie

Technique used:

Cube with card triangle corners, incorporating a motor.

Equipment needed:
- low melt glue gun
- 8mm or 10mm square section wood
- pva glue
- motor pulley
- junior hacksaw
- automatic wire cutters and strippers

- felt pens
- motor
- card triangles
- bench hook
- wire

How to make the example:

Step 1. Photocopy the sheet opposite onto card or paste onto card, one per child.

Step 2. Cut out the clown and the bow tie along the solid black lines.

Step 3. Decorate the clown and the bow tie.

Step 4. Cut 8 pieces of wood which measure 10cms in length.

Step 5. Lay 4 pieces of the cut wood down on a flat surface as in the diagram. Glue 4 triangles in position as described on the previous page.

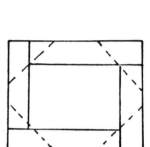

Step 6. Turn over the frame and glue 4 more triangles in the corner positions.

Step 7. Repeat the process with the other 4 pieces of wood. These two frames will form the top and bottom of the cuboid.

Step 8. Cut 4 pieces of wood that measure 5 cms in length. These four pieces will form the sides of the cuboid that is to be constructed.

Step 9. Using the card triangles, glue the four sides into place as in the diagram. Two triangles must be glued in place at the top of the side sections and two triangles at the bottom.

Step 10. Allow the cuboid to dry.

Step 11. Glue a motor with the glue gun in the middle of one of the sides on the top section making sure that the shaft is sticking out over the end of the cuboid. Secure in place by wrapping masking tape around the motor and the frame.

Step 12. Attach the wires to the motor and connect to a battery as previously described.

Step 13. Make a hole through the black dot marked 'A' on the clown and push this hole over the drive shaft of the motor. Glue the clown to the wooden frame.

Step 14. Push a small black pulley onto the protruding drive shaft and glue the decorated bow tie onto the pulley.

Step 15. Connect the wires to the battery terminals and watch the bow tie spin.

How the idea may be developed:

The pupils can design their own pictures which can have spinning parts.

Experiment with lights. Could the clowns eyes and nose be made to light up?

A

Railway Signal

Technique used:

Levers, pneumatics and hydraulics.

Equipment needed:

low melt, cool glue gun
4mm dowel   strip wood   2mm drill bit
plastic tubing   10ml syringe   sticky tape
drill with 6mm drill bit   florists wire   wooden base

How to make the example:

Step 1.   Cut a piece of strip wood which is 18cms long.
Step 2.   Drill a hole 2cms from the end of the piece of wood with the drill fitted with the 6mm drill bit.
Step 3.   Glue the undrilled end of the piece of strip wood onto the middle of the wooden base. Reinforce as shown on page 18.
Step 4.   Photocopy the sheet opposite, one per child.
Step 5.   Cut out the striped barrier arms, decorate and paste onto pieces of strip wood which are of the same length as the arms - 15cms.
Step 6.   Drill through the holes marked A on the barrier arms with the 6mm drill bit. These holes are in the position of the pivot and small movements can be amplified by the position of the pivot.
Step 7.   Drill through the holes marked B on all the barrier arms with the 2mm drill bit.
Step 8.   Cut a piece of dowel 3cms long.
Step 9.   Cut 2 pieces of plastic tubing 1 cm long.
Step 10.   Place the dowel through the drilled hole at the top of the upright strip wood and put a piece of the cut plastic tubing on the back of the dowel to stop it falling out of the strip wood.
Step 11.   Place the 5mm drilled hole of barrier arm 'i' onto the other end of the dowel and place the other piece of cut tubing onto the end of the arm to keep it in place. **NB The arm must be free moving.**
Step 12.   Attach a length of plastic tubing to the nozzle of a syringe and pull the plunger out. Attach the other end of the tubing to a second syringe which has the plunger pushed in.
Step 13.   Using sticky tape, attach the syringe with the plunger extended onto the upright strip wood as in the diagram.
Step 14.   Wrap one end of a piece of florists wire around the extended neck of the upright plunger and push the other end of the wire through the 2mm drilled hole at the end of the barrier arm. **NB Make sure the arm is in a horizontal position as in the diagram.**
Step 15.   Pull the plunger of the second syringe out and watch the barrier arm raise. Repeat the activity using all of the barrier arms. Which one works the best?

How the idea may be developed:

The tubing and one of the syringes can be filled with water so that the railway signal is operated by hydraulics (water) instead of pneumatics (air). Which works best?

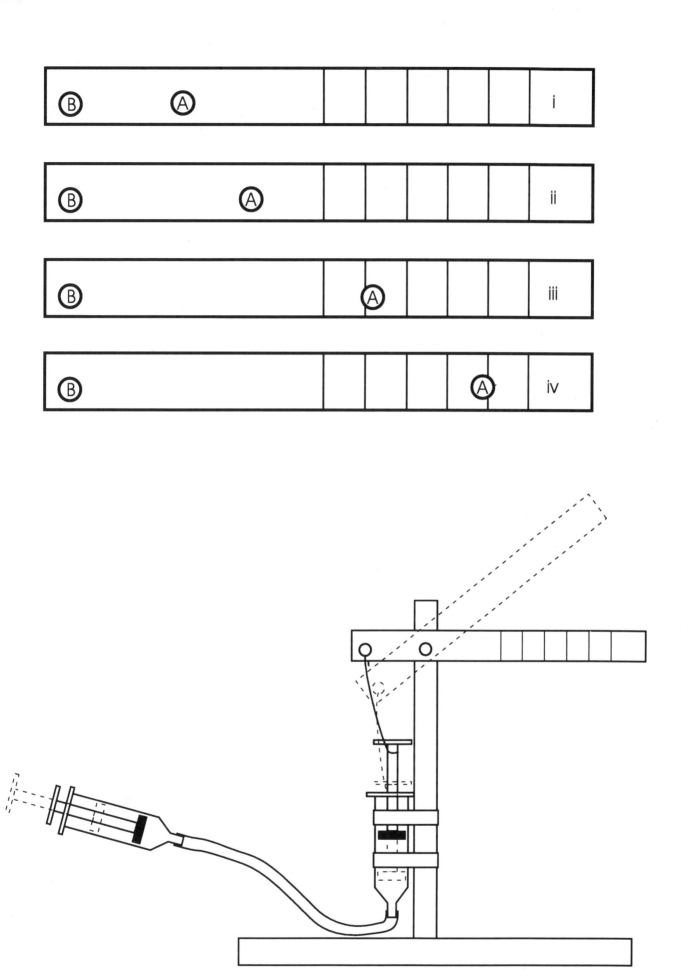

Tipper Truck

Technique used:

pneumatics.

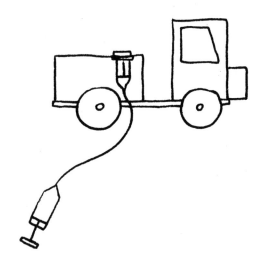

Equipment needed:

vehicle chassis	syringes
plastic tubing	boxes
sticky tape	card

How to make the example:

Step 1.   Make one of the vehicle chassis from the book.

Step 2.   Select a box or make a net that will fit onto the back of the chassis.

Step 3.   Using a piece of sticky tape, hinge the box onto the back of the chassis as in the diagram.

Step 4.   Glue a lolly stick across the top of the box ensuring it protrudes over the edge of the box, as in the diagram.

Step 5.   Push one end of a piece of tubing onto a syringe with the plunger pulled out and the other end of the tubing onto a syringe with the plunger pushed in.

Step 6.   Using sticky tape, attach the syringe with the plunger pushed in to the side of the vehicle chassis so that the plunger is positioned under the lolly stick.

Step 7.   Push the plunger of the second syringe down and watch the back of the truck tip up.

How the idea may be developed:

The children can experiment with other combinations of syringes as in the diagram. Can the pupils create a mouse that pops out of a hole?

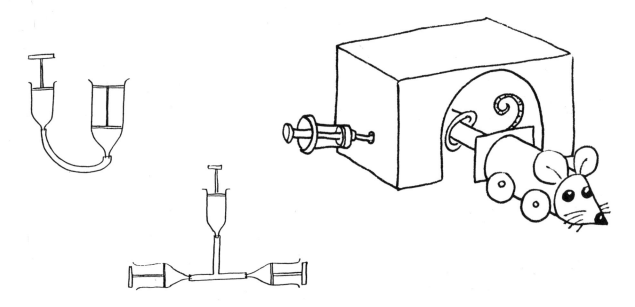